PROBLEMS IN DIFFERENTIAL EQUATIONS

A SERIES OF BOOKS IN MATHEMATICS

Editors: *R. A. Rosenbaum* *G. Philip Johnson*

PROBLEMS IN DIFFERENTIAL EQUATIONS

Second Edition

J. L. Brenner

STANFORD RESEARCH INSTITUTE

W. H. FREEMAN AND COMPANY

San Francisco and London

Adapted from

PROBLEMS IN DIFFERENTIAL EQUATIONS

by A. F. Filippov

Preface

At the beginning of every paragraph, the basic ideas needed for solving the problems that follow are given. Next, complete solutions of illustrative problems appear. For general theorems, and discussion of the more advanced material, the reader is referred at specific points to standard treatises on differential equations. Among these are

A A Andronow and C E Chaikin. Theory of Oscillations. Princeton University Press 1949

E A Coddington and N Levinson. Ordinary Differential Equations. New York: **McGraw-Hill** 1953   429 pp.

E Kamke. Differentialgleichungen. Lösungsmethoden und Lösungen. Band 1. Gewöhnliche Differentialgleichungen. 3 Aufl. New York: Chelsea 1948   666 pp.   \$9.50

N N Krasovskii. Theory of Motion. Translated by J L Brenner. Stanford University Press 1963

S Lefschetz and J LaSalle. Stability Theory of Differential Equations. Prentice-Hall 1962

V V Nemytskii and V V Stepanov. Qualitative Theory of Differential Equations. Translated under the Direction of S Lefschetz. Princeton University Press 1960

F G Tricomi. Differential Equations. Translated
by E A McHarg. Glasgow: Blackie 1961
50 shillings.

Other texts, of varying degrees of difficulty, are the

following:

R P Agnew. Differential Equations 2nd Ed.
New York: McGraw-Hill 1960   485 pp. $7.50

H S Bear. Differential Equations.
Reading, Mass: Addison-Wesley 1962   207 pp. $7.50

G Birkhoff and G C Rota. Ordinary differential equations.
Boston: Ginn 1962   318 pp. $8.50

E A Coddington. An introduction to ordinary differential
equations. Englewood Cliffs, New Jersey:
Prentice-Hall 1961   292 pp. $9.00

L Collatz. Numerische Behandlung von Differentialgleichungen. Berlin: Springer 1955

S V Fagg. Differential Equations. New York: Harper
and Row   1961   127 pp. $1.35

L R Ford. Differential Equations 2nd Ed.
New York: McGraw-Hill 1955   291 pp. $6.50

D Greenspan. Theory and Solution of Ordinary Differential
Equations. New York: MacMillan 1960 148 pp. $5.50

P Henrici. Discrete Variable Methods in Ordinary
Differential Equations. New York: Wiley 1962
407 pp. $9.95

F B Hildebrand.   Introduction to Numerical Analysis.
New York: McGraw-Hill 1956.

W Kaplan. Ordinary Differential Equations.
Reading, Mass: Addison-Wesley 1958   534 pp. plus
loose errata sheet. $9.75

S Lefschetz. Differential Equations: Geometric
Theory 2nd Ed. New York: Interscience 1963
390 pp. $10.00

C W Leininger. Differential Equations. New York:
Harper 1962   271 pp. $6.00

W T Martin and E Reissner. Elementary Differential
Equations. 2nd Ed   Reading, Mass: Addison-Wesley
1961   260 pp. $7.50

M Morris and O E Brown. Differential Equations   3rd Ed.
Prentice-Hall 1952 $11.35

A L Nelson, K W Folley, M Coral.   Differential Equations
2nd Ed.   Boston: Heath 1960   308 pp.

H B Phillips. Differential Equations. New York:
Wiley 1934   125 pp.

E D Rainville. Elementary Differential Equations
New York: Macmillan 1958   449 pp. $6.00

M Tenenbaum and H Pollard.   Ordinary Differential
Equations. New York: Harper and Row 1963
791 pp. $10.75

L R Wilcox and H J Curtis. Elementary Differential
Equations.   Scranton, Pa: International Textbook
Co. 1961   273 pp. $8.00

Many of the problems are routine, but each serves its special purpose.   There is a liberal sprinkling of non-routine
problems also; the more difficult ones are indicated by stars.

The explanations are so extensive that this book is almost a complete course in itself. The only thing missing is complete proofs of the more complicated existence and approximation theorems.

Beginning students are sometimes handicapped by becoming <u>married</u> to the use of certain letters, such as x for the independent variable. It is good practice to translate problems from one notation to another and back. For example, to integrate the expression $x + \cos x$, change the problem to: "integrate the expression $t + \cos t$," obtain the answer $C + \frac{1}{2} t^2 + \sin t$, and finally, report the answer $C + \frac{1}{2} x^2 + \sin x$. This changes the marriage from one of necessity to one of convenience.

Preface to Second Edition

Besides correcting typographical errors and rearranging certain material, I have added two appendices. The second of these is standard material showing the formalism of the Laplace transform applied to the solution of linear differential equations with constant coefficients. This material has been added in response to several requests.

The first appendix is an extensive, logically complete discussion of the existence and uniqueness of the solution of a linear differential equation with constant coefficients, together with theory and practice exemplified by several problems. As far as I know, no other publication obtains the result without using the ideas of Wronskian and linear dependence. These ideas are not in themselves abhorrent, but perhaps the student should learn one thing at a time.

J. L. Brenner

CONTENTS

INTRODUCTION

The term "differential equation" is a generic term that describes
a certain body of subject matter. The concern of this book is almost
wholly with a differential equation of the type

$$y' = f(x,y),$$

where f is a differentiable function of its arguments in a certain
region.

By a solution of this differential equation is meant a function $\phi(x)$
of a single independent variable that is differentiable for those values
of the independent variable that lie in the given region, and such that
the relation

$$\phi' = f(\phi(x),x)$$

holds for the values of x that come into question. Exact statements of
this definition, and proofs of the existence of solutions, will be found
in the references.

A more general type of "differential equation" is the system

$$y' = f(x,y,z), \qquad z' = g(x,y,z),$$

for which a <u>solution</u> is defined in a corresponding manner; in this case
a solution is a pair of functions $\phi(x)$, $\psi(x)$.

Thus the set

$$y' = z$$

$$z' = - P(x)y' - Q(x)y + R(x)$$

is equivalent to the single equation

$$y'' + P(x) \, y' + Q(x) \, y = R(x)$$

in a region in which all the functions involved are defined.

In studying this page, a student will do well to rewrite the discussion in terms of a new set of letters.

THINGS TO REVIEW

Definition of derivative, and standard formulas for derivatives of elementary functions and combinations of functions, must be at hand. Some of the formulas are included at the back of this book. Certain formulas of integration are given there too; for some problems it may be convenient to have a more extensive table of integrals.

Abbreviated tables of the elementary functions are also given at the back of the book.

Section I

ISOCLINES. CONSTRUCTION OF THE DIFFERENTIAL EQUATION
FOR A FAMILY OF CURVES. ISOGONAL TRAJECTORIES

If the differential equation $y' = f(x,y)$, is satisfied by a curve
going through the point (x,y), then the tangent line to the curve at the
point in question must have slope y', that is the angle α which this
line makes with the x axis must satisfy $\alpha = \arctan f(x,y)$. The geometric locus of those points for which $y' = f(x,y)$ has a constant value
k is called an isocline. Thus the equations of the isoclines are
$f(x,y) = k$, where k is constant on each isocline.

To solve the differential equation $y' = f(x,y)$ geometrically, it
is sufficient to draw a number of isoclines and to sketch a curve which
crosses each isocline with the correct slope. Examples of this construction are given in any elementary text on differential equations.

The loci which intersect every curve of a given family of curves at
a constant preassigned angle ϕ are called isogonal trajectories. The
angle β which the trajectory makes with the x axis is thus ϕ units
greater or less than the angle α which the intersected trajectory makes
with the same axis: $\beta = \alpha \pm \phi$. Suppose

$$y' = f(x,y) \tag{1}$$

is the differential equation corresponding to a particular family of

curves and suppose

$$y_1' = f_1(x,y) \qquad ($$

is the differential equation of a family of isogonal trajectories. In

other words, $\tan \alpha = f(x,y)$, $\tan \beta = f_1(x,y)$. Thus when equation (

and the angle ϕ are given it is easy to write down the formula for

$\tan \beta$, and thus to set up the differential equation (2) from which the

isogonal trajectories are to be found.

If the equation of the given family is written in the form

$F(x,y,y') = 0$, then only slight changes are needed in the above method

to write down the differential equation of the isogonal trajectories.

The formulas needed for the above work are

$$y' = \tan \beta = \frac{\tan \alpha \pm \tan \phi}{1 \mp \tan \alpha \tan \phi} \qquad (2$$

Suppose the equation

$$F(x,y,C_1,\ldots,C_n) = 0 \qquad ($$

of a family of curves is given. To construct the differential equation

of this family, we differentiate equation (3) n times, and eliminate

the constants $C_1,\ldots,C_n$ from the equations so obtained.

Example. Let the given family have equation

$$C_1 x + (y - C_2)^2 = 0. \qquad ($$

This equation contains two parameters so we differentiate it twice as follows:

$$C_1 + 2(y - C_2)y' = 0, \tag{5}$$

$$2y'^2 + 2(y - C_2)y'' = 0. \tag{6}$$

Let us eliminate C_1. From equation (5) we obtain $C_1 = -2(y-C_2)y'$; putting this into equation (4) we get

$$- 2xy' (y - C_2) + (y - C_2) = 0. \tag{7}$$

Now we eliminate C_2. From equation (6) we get $y - C_2 = -\dfrac{y'^2}{y''}$; substituting this in (7), we obtain finally the differential equation we need $y' + 2xy'' = 0$.

In problems 1-14 use the method of isoclines to solve the differential equation given.

1. $y' = y - x^2$.
2. $2(y + y') = x + 3$.
3. $y' = \dfrac{x^2 + y^2}{2} - 1$.
4. $(x^2 + 1) y' = y - 2x$.
5. $yy' + x = 0$.
6. $xy' = 2y$.
7. $xy' + y = 0$.
8. $y' + 1 = 2(y - x)(y' - 1)$.
9. $y'(y^2 + 1) + x = 0$.
10. $y' = \dfrac{x}{y}$.
11. $y' = \dfrac{y - 3x}{x + 3y}$.
12. $y' = \dfrac{y}{x + y}$.
13. $x^2 + y^2 y' = 1$.
14. $(x^2 + y^2) y' = 4x$.

15. Give the equation of the locus of points which are maximum or minimum points of solutions of the equation $y' = f(x,y)$. What is the analytic description of a maximum or minimum point?

16. Give a method for finding the locus of the inflection points of the solutions of the equation $y' = f(x,y)$.

In problems 17-29 find the differential equations which correspon
to the following families of curves.

17. $y = e^{Cx}$. 18. $y = (x - C)^3$. 19. $y = Cx^3$.

20. $y = \sin(x+C)$. 21. $x^2 + Cy^2 = 2y$.

22. $y^2 + Cx = x^3$. 23. $y = C(x-C)^2$.

24. $Cy = \sin Cx$. 25. $y = ax^2 + be^x$.

26. $(x - a)^2 + by^2 = 1$. 27. $y = a \sin x + bx$.

28. $y = ax^3 + bx^2 + cx$. 29. $x = ay^2 + by + c$.

30. Write the differential equation of circles of radius 1 whi
have centers on the line $y = 2x$.

31. Find the differential equation of the parabolas that have
axis parallel to the y axis and that are tangent to the two lines
$y = 0$, $y = x$.

32. Find the differential equation of the circles which are
tangent to the lines $y = 0$, $y = x$, and lie entirely in the sector
$0 \leqq y \leqq x$.

33. Write the differential equation of all parabolas which have
axis parallel to the y axis and pass through the origin.

34. Write the differential equation of all circles which are
tangent to the x axis.

In problems 35 and 36 find the system of differential equations which is satisfied by the given family of curves.

35. $ax + z = b$, $y^2 + z^2 = b^2$.

36. $x^2 + y^2 = z^2 - 2bz$; $y = ax + b$.

In problems 37-50 find the differential equations of the trajectories which intersect the given family isogonally at the angle ϕ :

37. $y = Cx^4$, $\varphi = 90°$.   **38.** $y^2 = x + C$, $\varphi = 90°$.

39. $x^2 = y + Cx$, $\varphi = 90°$.   **40.** $x^2 + y^2 = a^2$, $\varphi = 45°$.

41. $y = kx$, $\varphi = 60°$.   **42.** $3x^2 + y^2 = C$, $\varphi = 30°$.

43. $y^2 = 2px$, $\varphi = 60°$.   **44.** $r = a + \cos\theta$, $\varphi = 90°$.

45. $r = a\cos^2\theta$, $\varphi = 90°$.   **46.** $r = a\sin\theta$, $\varphi = 45°$.

47. $y = x\ln x + Cx$, $\varphi = \text{arctg}\,2$.

48. $x^2 + y^2 = 2ax$, $\varphi = 45°$.

49. $x^2 + C^2 = 2Cy$, $\varphi = 90°$.   **50.** $y = Cx + C^3$, $\varphi = 90°$.

EQUATIONS IN WHICH THE VARIABLES ARE SEPARABLE

A differential equation in which the variables are separable will take one of the forms

$$y' = f(x) \, g(y),\tag{1}$$

$$M(x) \, N(y) \, dx + P(x) \, Q(y) \, dy = 0.\tag{2}$$

To solve such an equation it is only necessary to rewrite it so that one of the variables and its differential is missing from one side and the other variable and its differential is missing from the other side

Example. Solve the differential equation

$$x^2 y^2 y' + 1 = y.\tag{3}$$

This can be written in the form above as follows

$$x^2 y^2 \, \frac{dy}{dx} = y - 1; \quad x^2 y^2 dy = (y - 1) \, dx.$$

If we divide this last equation by $x^2 \, (y-1)$, we obtain

$$\frac{y^2}{y - 1} \, dy = \frac{dx}{x^2} \ .$$

The variables are separated. Integrating each side separately we obtain

$$\int \frac{y^2}{y - 1} \, dy = \int \frac{dx}{x^2} \ ; \ \frac{y^2}{2} + y + \ln\left|y - 1\right| = - \frac{1}{x} + C.$$

Since we have divided $x^2(y-1)$ we must try separately each of the solutions $x = 0$, $y - 1 = 0$. It is clear that $y = 1$ is a solution of equation (3), while $x = 0$ is not.

An equation of the form $y' = f(ax+by)$ can be transformed into an equation with separable variables by making the substitution $z = ax + by$, or $z = ax + by + c$, where c is an arbitrary constant.

In problems 51-65, solve the given equations and draw some integral curves in each case. State which solutions satisfy the initial conditions prescribed in those cases where initial conditions are given.

51. $xydx + (x+1)\,dy = 0$. 52. $\sqrt{y^2+1}\,dx = xydy$.

53. $(x^2 - 1)\,y' + 2xy^2 = 0$; $y(0) = 1$.

54. $y'\,ctg\,x + y = 2$; $y(0) = -1$.

55. $y' = 3\sqrt[3]{y^2}$; $y(2) = 0$. 56. $xy' + y = y^2$; $y(1) = 0.5$.

57. $2x^2yy' + y^2 = 2$. 58. $y' - xy^2 = 2xy$.

59. $e^{-s}\left(1 + \dfrac{ds}{dt}\right) = 1$. 60. $z' = 10^{x+z}$.

61. $x\,\dfrac{ux}{dt} + t = 1$. 62. $y' = \cos(y - x)$.

63. $y' - y = 2x - 3$. 64. $(x+2y)\,y' = 1$; $y(0) = -1$.

65. $y' = \sqrt{4x + 2y - 1}$.

In problems 66-67 find the solution of the equations which satisfies the given conditions for $x \to +\infty$.

66. $x^2\,y' - \cos 2y = 1$; $y(+\infty) = \dfrac{9}{4}\pi$.

67. $3y^2y' + 16x = 2xy^3$; $y(x)$ is bounded for $x \to +\infty$

68. Find the orthogonal trajectories which correspond to the following families:

a) $y = Cx^2$; b) $y = Ce^x$; c) $Cx^2 + y^2 = 1$.

In problems 69^* and 70^* the variables can be separated but the resulting equations cannot be integrated by elementary functions. Thus answers to the questions posed must be obtained by a limiting process.

69^*. Show that every integral curve of the equation

$$y' = \sqrt[3]{\frac{y^2 + 1}{x^4 + 1}}$$

has two horizontal asymptotes.

70^*. Discuss the behavior of the integral curves of the equation

$$y' = \sqrt{\frac{\ln(1 + y)}{\sin x}}$$

in the neighborhood of the origin. Show that from every point on the boundary of the first quadrant there is an integral curve which points into this quadrant.

GEOMETRICAL AND PHYSICAL PROBLEMS

Note: All the problems in this paragraph lead to equations in which variables can be separated. Other exercises involving physical problems are in Section 17.

The first step in solving the geometrical problems in this section is to think of the required curve as having the equation $y = y(x)$ if cartesian coordinates are to be used, and to find the analytical form of the properties the curve is required to have. In all problems the coordinates and slopes are denoted by x, y, y'. The second step is to solve the differential equation which rewrites the problem in analytical form.

In the physical problems the first step is to determine which quantities are variables and give them names. The time, the concentration or some other quantity is the independent variable, and the dependent variable is another quantity which varies in a regular fashion with the independent variable. The derivative appears as the quotient of the difference $y(x + \Delta x) - y(x)$ by Δx. Sometimes it is the task of the solver to take the step of dividing a given relation by Δx and determining the limit of this quotient as Δx approaches 0. The difference quotient represents rate of change. The derivative represents instantaneous rate. In particular, the derivative dy/dt is velocity or rate of change of the dependent variable y with respect to the time t .

In some problems the student must set up the differential equation on the basis of the physical law which is given in the text of the problem.

Example. A flask contains 10 liters of water and to it is being added a salt solution that contains 0.3 kilograms of salt per liter. This salt solution is being poured in at the rate of 2 liters per minute. The solution is being thoroughly mixed and drained off, and the mixture is drained off at the same rate so that the flask contains 10 liters at all times. How much salt is in the flask after five minutes?

Solution. The independent variable most convenient for this problem is t, and y is the dependent variable representing the number of kilograms of salt in the flask at the end of t minutes:

$$y = y(t).$$

The amount of salt added to the flask between time   t   and time

t + Δt is computed as follows.   Each minute two liters of solu-

tion is added so that in Δt   minutes, 2Δt   liters are added.

In these   2Δt   liters the amount of salt is (0.3)· 2Δt = 0.6 Δt

kilograms of salt.   On the other hand   2Δt   liters of solution

are withdrawn from the flask in an interval Δt.   Now at the

moment   t   the 10 liters in the flask contain   y(t) kilograms of

salt.   Therefore   2Δt of these liters contain   0.2 Δt · y(t)

kilograms of salt, if we suppose that the amount of salt does

not change in the short period of time Δt.   This is almost true

when Δt is a very short interval.   Indeed if the correct for-

mula for the last quantity is   0.2 Δt (y+α) kilograms, then

$\alpha \to 0$ for Δt $\to 0$.

We have computed the amount of salt added in the interval

(t,t+Δt), as well as the amount subtracted in the same interval.

But the difference between the amounts of salt present at times

t+Δt,   t   is   y(t+Δt) - y(t), and we have obtained the equation

$$y(t+\Delta t) - y(t) = 0.6\Delta t - 0.2\Delta t \cdot (y(t)+\alpha).$$

We now divide by Δt   and let Δt$\to 0$.   The left member approaches

the derivative   y'(t), and the right member approaches 0.6 —

0.2 y(t).   The differential equation is thus:

$$y'(t) = 0.6 - 0.2 \, y(t),$$

and its solution is

$$y(t) = 3 - Ce^{-0.2t}. \qquad (1)$$

When t is zero, the amount of salt in the flask is zero, that is $y(0) = 0$. Equation (1) shows that when $t = 0$, we have

$$y(0) = 3 - C; \quad 0 = 3 - C; \quad C = 3.$$

The value of C is now known, so that equation (1) reads

$$y(t) = 3 - 3e^{-0.2t}.$$

To find y at the end of five minutes, we simply substitute $t = 5$ and obtain

$$y(5) = 3 - 3e^{-0.2 \cdot 5} = 3 - 3e^{-1} \approx 1.9 \text{ kilograms of salt.}$$

71. Find a curve for which the area of the triangle determined by the tangent, the ordinate to the point of tangency and the x axis has a constant value equal to a^2 .

72. Find a curve for which the sum of the sides of a triangle constructed as in the previous problem has a constant value equal to b.

73. Find a curve with the following property. The segment of the x axis included between the tangent and normal at any point on the curve is equal to 2a.

74. Find a curve such that the point of intersection of an arbitrary tangent with the x axis has an abscissa half as great as the abscissa of the point of tangency.

75. Find a curve with the following property. If through an arbitrary point of the curve parallels are drawn to the coordinate axes and meet these axes forming a rectangle, the area of this rectangle is divided by the curve in the ratio 1:2.

76. Find a curve such that the tangent at an arbitrary point makes equal angles with the radius vector and the polar axis (principal direction).

In problems 77-79 it is supposed that the amount of gas (or liquid) contained in any fixed volume is constant. Also thorough mixing is assumed.

77. A 20 liter vessel contains air (80% nitrogen and 20% oxygen). 0.1 liters of nitrogen is added to the container per second. If continual mixing takes place and material is withdrawn at the rate at which it is added, how long will it be before the container holds 99% nitrogen?

78. A 100 liter beaker contains 10 kilograms of salt. Water is added at the constant rate of 5 liters per minute with complete mixing, and drawn off at the same rate. How much salt

is in the beaker after one hour?

79. A large chamber contains 200 cubic meters of gas,
0.15% of which is carbon dioxide (CO_2). A ventilator exchanges
20 cubic meters per minute of this gas with new gas containing
only 0.04% CO_2. How long will it be before the concentration of
CO_2 is reduced to half its original value?

In problems 80-82 one must use Newton's law of cooling,
which says that the rate of change of temperature is proportional
to the difference of temperature between a cooling body and its
surroundings.

80. A body cools in 10 minutes from 100° to 60°. The
surroundings are at a temperature of 20°. When will the body
cool to 25°?

81. A container holds 1 kilogram of water at 20°. A 0.5
kilogram mass of aluminum is added at 75°. The heat capacity
of aluminum is 0.2. In 1 minute's time the water is warmed 2^O.
When did the aluminum cool by 1^O, and when did the water warm
by 1^O? Assume that the water loses no heat to its surroundings.
To say that the specific heat of aluminum is 0.2 means that 1
kilogram of aluminum contains as much heat as 0.2 kilograms of
water.

82. A slug of metal at a temperature of 80° is put in an oven, the temperature of which is gradually warmed during an hour from a° to b°. Find the temperature of the metal at the end of an hour, assuming that the metal warms kT degrees per minute when it finds itself in an oven which is T degrees warmer.

83. A raft is being slowed down by resistance of the water, the resistance being proportional to the speed of the raft. If the initial speed was 1.5 meters per second and at the end of 4 seconds was 1 meter per second, when will the speed decrease to 1 centimeter per second? What total distance will the raft travel?

Problems 84-86 concern radioactive decay. The decay law states that the amount of radioactive substance that decays is proportional at each instant to the amount of substance present.

84. The strength of a radioactive substance decreases 50% in a 30-day period. How long will it take for the radioactivity to decrease to 1% of its initial value?

85. It is experimentally determined that every gram of radium loses 0.44 milligrams in 1 year. What length of time elapses before the radioactivity decreases to half its original value?

86. A certain piece of mineral contains 100 milligrams of uranium and 14 milligrams of uranium lead. It is known that uranium loses half its radioactivity in $4.5 \cdot 10^9$ years and the original amount of 238 grams of uranium decays to 206 grams of uranium lead. Calculate the mineral's age. Assume that when the mineral was born it contained no lead. Also, neglect the intermediate products of composition since the products to which uranium decomposes change themselves much more rapidly than uranium does.

87. The amount of light absorbed by a thin layer of water is proportional to the amount of incident light, and to the thickness of the layer. If a layer of water 35 cm thick absorbs half the light incident on its surface, what proportion of the incident light will be absorbed by a layer of water 200 cm thick?

In problems 88-90 it will be convenient to take the velocity to be the unknown function. Take the acceleration of gravity to be 10 m-sec^{-2}.

88. Air resistance is proportional to the square of velocity. The terminal velocity of fall of a human in air of standard density is 50 m/ sec. Neglecting the variation of air

density with altitude, find when a man's parachute should be

opened, assuming that he falls from an altitude of 1.5 km, and

his parachute must open when he reaches an altitude of 0.5 km.

89. The mass of a football is 0.4 kg. Air resists passage of the ball, the resistive force being proportional to the
square of the velocity, and being equal to 0.48 kg when the
velocity if 1 m/sec. Find the height to which the ball will
rise, and the time to reach that height, if it is thrown upwards with a velocity of 20 m/sec. How is the answer altered
if air resistance be neglected?

90. The football of the preceding exercise is released
(from rest) at an altitude of 16.3 m. Find its final velocity and time of fall.

In problems 91-95, assume that water emerging from an
aperture in a vessel has velocity $0.6 \sqrt{2gh}$ m/sec, where
$g = 10$ m.sec^{-2} is the force of gravity, and h is the height of
the surface of the water above the aperture.

91. A vertical cylindrical vessel has diameter $2R = 1.8$ m
and height $H = 2.45$ m. How long will it take to empty the
vessel through a hole in the bottom of diameter $2r = 6$ cm?

92.   Answer the same question if the axis of the cylinder is horizontal, and the hole is at a lowest point.

93.   A cylindrical beaker with vertical axis can be half drained through a hole in the bottom in 5 minutes. How long would it take to empty the beaker completely?

94.   A conical funnel has radius R = 6 cm and height H = 10 cm. If the opening of the funnel is a circle of diameter 0.5 cm, how long will it take to empty the entire funnel if it is initially full of water?

95.   A rectangular vessel has base 60 cm by 75 cm, and height 80 cm, with an opening in the bottom 2.5 cm^2 in area. Water is being added to it at the rate of 1.8 liters per second (1 liter = 1000 cm^3.) How long does it take to fill the vessel? Compare the answer with the result that would be obtained on neglecting the hole in the bottom.

96.   A uniform extensible cord 1 m long is stretched kf meters by a force of f kg. A cord of the same material l meters long has mass P kg. If it is suspended by one end, how much is it extended under the weight of its own mass?

97.   The density of air is 0.0012 g/cm^3. Neglecting any variation in temperature, pressure is proportional to the

density, and is 1 kg/cm^2 at the earth's surface. Find the

pressure as a function of the height h.

98. A boat is held by a cable that is wound around a post,

the end being held by a laborer. What is the braking force in

the cable if it is wound around the post three times, the

coefficient of friction between cable and post is 1/3, and the

laborer exerts a force of 10 kg on the free end of the cable?

99. A closed vessel with volume v m^3 contains liquid

water and air. The speed of evaporation of the water is pro-

portional to the difference between the saturation concentration

q_1 of water vapor (amount per m^3) at the given temperature, and the

amount q of water vapor per m^3 actually present in the air (assume

that the temperature of the air and water, and the amount of

area on which evaporation occurs does not change). Initially

there are m_O grams of water in the vessel, and q_O grams of

vapor in each m^3 of air. How much water remains in the vessel

at the end of t units of time?

100. The mass of a rocket, including a full chamber of

fuel, is M; its net mass (without fuel) is m. The products

of combustion are ejected with velocity c. If the rocket

starts from rest, find Ciolkovskii's formula, which gives the speed imparted to the rocket by the burning of the fuel, neg-

lecting the resistance of the atmosphere.

Section 4

HOMOGENEOUS EQUATIONS

A homogeneous equation is one that can be written in the
form $y' = f(y/x)$ or in the form $M(x,y)\ dx + N(x,y)\ dy = 0$,
where $M(x,y)$ and $N(x,y)$ are homogeneous functions of the
same degree. Here, a function $M(x,y)$ is called a homogeneous
function of degree n, if the equation $M(kx,\ ky) = k^n M(x,y)$
holds for every value of k. Such an equation can be solved
by making the substitution $y = tx$. This substitution reduces
the equation to an equation in which the variables are separable.

Example. Solve the equation $x\ dy = (x+y)\ dx$.

This is a homogeneous equation. The substitution $y = tx$
leads to the equation $dy = tdx + xdt$. When this is substituted
in the original equation, the result

$$x(xdt + tdx) = (x + tx)\ dx; \quad xdt = dx$$

is obtained. The variables are immediately separable; the
equation is written

$$dt = dx/x; \quad t = \ln\left| x \right| + C.$$

Last, we introduce the original variable y, and obtain the equation $y = x(\ln |x| + C)$. Besides this solution there is a singular solution $x = 0$, which was lost when we divided by x.

An equation of the form $y' = f\left(\dfrac{a_1 x + b_1 y + c_1}{ax + by + c}\right)$ can be made homogeneous by translating the origin to the point of intersection of the lines that have equations $ax + by + c = 0$, $a_1 x + b_1 y + c_1 = 0$. If, however, these lines do not intersect the relation $a_1 x + b_1 y = k(ax + by)$ must hold. Thus the original equation has the form $y' = F(ax + by)$ and is easily converted to a form with separable variables by substituting $z = ax + by$, or $z = ax + by + c$. See Section 2.

If the number m is correctly chosen, some equations can be written in homogeneous form by making the substitution $y = z^m$. It is usually better to determine m by examining the result of the substitution. It should be remarked that this substitution is unsuccessful for the value $m = 0$.

Example. Consider the equation
$$2x^4 yy' + y^4 = 4x^6.$$
The substitution $y = z^m$ gives the new equation
$$2mx^4 z^{2m-1} z' + z^{4m} = 4x^6.$$

This equation is homogeneous if and only if all the terms have

the same degree. This would require

$$4+(2m-1) = 4m = 6.$$

The value $m = 3/2$ does satisfy both requirements. Thus the

substitution $y = z^{3/2}$ renders the original equation homogeneous.

Solve equations 101-129.

101. $(x+2y)\,dx - x\,dy = 0.$
102. $(x-y)\,dx + (x+y)\,dy = 0.$
103. $(y^2-2xy)\,dx + x^2\,dy = 0.$ **104.** $2x^3y' = y(2x^2-y^2).$
105. $y^2 + x^2y' = xyy'.$ **106.** $(x^2+y^2)\,y' = 2xy.$

107. $xy' - y = x\,\mathrm{tg}\,\dfrac{y}{x}.$ **108.** $xy' = y - xe^{\frac{y}{x}}.$

109. $xy' - y = (x+y)\ln\dfrac{x+y}{x}.$ **110.** $xy' = y\cos\ln\dfrac{y}{x}.$

111. $\left(y+\sqrt{xy}\right)dx = x\,dy.$ **112.** $xy' = \sqrt{x^2-y^2} + y.$
113. $(2x-4y+6)\,dx + (x+y-3)\,dy = 0.$
114. $(2x+y+1)\,dx - (4x+2y-3)\,dy = 0.$
115. $x-y-1 + (y-x+2)\,y' = 0.$
116. $(x+4y)\,y' = 2x+3y-5.$
117. $(y+2)\,dx = (2x+y-4)\,dy.$ **118.** $y' = 2\left(\dfrac{y+2}{x+y-1}\right)^2$

119. $(y'+1)\ln\dfrac{y+x}{x+3} = \dfrac{y+x}{x+3}.$

120. $y' = \dfrac{y+2}{x+1} + \mathrm{tg}\,\dfrac{y-2x}{x+1}.$

121. $x^3(y'-x) = y^2.$ **122.** $2x^2y' = y^3 + xy.$
123. $2x\,dy + (x^2y^4+1)\,y\,dx = 0.$
124. $y\,dx + x(2xy+1)\,dy = 0.$
125. $2y' + x = 4\sqrt{y}.$ **126.** $y' = y^2 - \dfrac{2}{x^2}.$
127. $2xy' + y = y^2\sqrt{x-x^2y^2}.$
128. $\dfrac{2}{3}xyy' = \sqrt{x^6-y^4} + y^2.$
129. $2y + (x^2y+1)\,xy' = 0.$

130. Find the trajectories which intersect the curves of

a given family at a 45° angle where the angle is measured from the tangent to the curve to the tangent to the trajectory drawn

in the negative direction.

a) $y = x \ln Cx$;   b) $(x-3y)^4 = Cxy^6$.

131. Find a curve for which the tangent intersects the

x axis at a point which is at the same distance from the origin

as from the point of tangency.

132. Find a curve for which the distance of an arbitrary

tangent from the origin is equal to the abscissa to the point

of tangency.

133. For what values of α, β can or does the substitu-

tion $y = z^m$ render the differential equation $y' = ax^\alpha + by^\beta$

homogeneous?

134.* Let the equation $f(k) = k$ have the root k_o. Show

the following.

1. If $f'(k_o) < 1$, then the line $y < k x$ is tangent

to no solution of the differential equation $y' = f(y/x)$.

2. If $f'(k_o) > 1$, then the line $y = k_o x$ is tangent

to infinitely many solutions of the same differential equation.

135.* Find conditions which are necessary and sufficient

to guarantee that every solution of the homogeneous equation

$y' = f(y/x)$ is a closed curve containing the origin.

Hint. Change the equation to polar coordinates.

Section 5

LINEAR FIRST ORDER EQUATIONS

The equation

$$y' + a(x) \, y = b(x) \tag{1}$$

is called linear. It is conveniently solved by considering

the auxiliary (reduced) equation

$$y' + a(x) \, y = 0. \tag{2}$$

This equation is one in which the variables are separable (See

Section 2). If the constant C obtained in solving this equa-

tion is replaced by an unknown function $C(x)$, and the putative

solution is substituted in equation (1), it will be possible to

determine the unknown function so that equation (1) is satisfied.

Some equations become linear if the dependent and indepen-

dent variables are interchanged; for example, the equation

$$y = (2x + y^3) \, y'$$

is nonlinear when x is thought of as the independent variable,

but if the equation is written in the form

$$y \, dx - (2x + y^3) \, dy = 0,$$

it becomes linear because this last form is equivalent to the

form

$$dx/dy - (2/y)x = y^2,$$

a linear equation with y as the independent variable. See

formula (1) above.

The Bernoulli equation

$$y' + a(x) \ y = b(x) \ y^n,$$

can be converted to the standard form above by dividing by y^n

and making the substitution $z = y^{1-n}$. The equation is then

solved for z in terms of x. The details are given in elemen-

tary books on differential equations.

The Riccati equation, (apparently first considered by

James Bernoulli, who gave fundamental algorithms for treating

it)

$$y' + a(x) \ y + b(x) \ y^2 = c(x)$$

cannot always be solved by quadratures. But if one solution

$y_1(x)$ is known, the substitution $y = y_1(x) + z$ converts the

Ricatti equation to a Bernoulli equation and thus the solution

can be completed by quadratures.

Certain equations can be written in a form free of the variable y. For example, a particular solution of the equation y' + y^2 = x^2 - 2x can be found by determining the parameters a, b so that y = ax + b is a solution. A second example is the following. The equation y' + 2y^2 = 6/x^2 has a particular solution y = a/x, which can be obtained by making the substitution y = a/x in the equation and determining a.

Solve the equations 136-160.

136. $xy' - 2y = 2x^4$.   **137.** $(2x + 1) y' = 4x + 2y$.
138. $y' + y \operatorname{tg} x = \sec x$.   **139.** $x (y' - y) = e^x$.
140. $x^2 y' + xy + 1 = 0$.   **141.** $y = x (y' - x \cos x)$.
142. $y' = 2x (x^2 + y)$.   **143.** $(xy' - 1) \ln x = 2y$.
144. $xy' + (x + 1) y = 3x^2 e^{-x}$.
145. $(x + y^2) dy = y \, dx$.   **146.** $(2e^y - x) y' = 1$.
147. $(\sin^2 y + x \operatorname{ctg} y) y' = 1$.
148. $(2x + y) dy = y \, dx + 4 \ln y \, dy$.

149. $y' = \dfrac{y}{3x - y^2}$.   **150.** $(1 - 2xy) y' = y (y - 1)$.
151. $y' + 2y = y^2 e^x$.   **152.** $(x + 1)(y' + y^2) = -y$.
153. $y' = y^4 \cos x + y \operatorname{tg} x$.   **154.** $xy^2 y' = x^2 + y^3$.
155. $xy \, dy = (y^2 + x) dx$.   **156.** $xy' - 2x^2 \sqrt{y} = 4y$.
157. $xy' + 2y + x^5 y^3 e^x = 0$.   **158.** $2y' - \dfrac{x}{y} = \dfrac{xy}{x^2 - 1}$.
159. $y' x^3 \sin y = xy' - 2y$.   **160.** $(2x^2 y \ln y - x) y' = y$.

Choose the appropriate independent variable in problems 161-166 so that the equation becomes linear, and solve the equation.

161. $x\,dx = (x^2 - 2y + 1)\,dy.$ **162.** $(x + 1)(yy' - 1) = y^2.$

163. $x(e^y - y') = 2.$

164. $(x^2 - 1)\,y'\sin y + 2x\cos y = 2x - 2x^3.$

165. $y(x) = \int_0^x y(t)\,dt + x + 1.$

166. $\int_0^x (x - t)\,y(t)\,dt = 2x + \int_0^x y(t)\,dt.$

In problems 167-171, find a particular solution, rewrite

the Ricatti equation as a Bernoulli equation and solve it.

167. $x^2 y' + xy + x^2 y^2 = 4.$ **168.** $3y' + y^2 + \dfrac{2}{x^2} = 0.$

169. $xy' - (2x + 1)\,y + y^2 = -x^2.$

170. $y' - 2xy + y^2 = 5 - x^2.$

171. $y' + 2ye^x - y^2 = e^{2x} + e^x.$

172. Find the curves which intersect the family

$$y^2 = Ce^x + x + 1.$$

orthogonally.

173. Find a curve such that the trapezoid bounded by the

coordinate axes, the tangent at an arbitrary point, and the

coordinate to that point has the constant area $3a^2$.

174. Find a curve such that the area of the triangle

bounded by a tangent at an arbitrary point, the x axis, and

the segment from the origin to the point of tangency has the

constant value a^2.

175. A 100-liter beaker contains 10 kilograms of salt. Five liters of water are added to the beaker per minute and the overflow, after perfect mixing, is conducted into another 100 liter beaker which initially contained pure water. The liquid in the second beaker is also perfectly mixed. When will the amount of salt in the second beaker reach its maximum and what is the value of this maximum?

176. Let Δt be a small quantity and written as a fraction of a year. In the time Δt, every gram of radium loses 0.00044 Δt grams and yields 0.00043 Δt grams of radon. In time Δt every gram of radon loses 70 Δt grams. At the beginning of a certain experiment, there is a quantity x_0 of pure radium. When will the amount of radon be a maximum?

177.* Find an approximate result indicating when the quantity of radon rises above 99% of its maximal value and when it again falls below 99% of its maximal value.

178. Find the solution of the equation

$$y' \sin 2x = 2(y + \cos x),$$

that remains bounded as $x \to \pi/2$.

179.* Show that the equation

$$\frac{dx}{dt} + x = f(t),$$

has a unique solution bounded for $-\infty < t < +\infty$, where $\left| f(t) \right| \leq$ M, $-\infty < t < +\infty$. Find the solution. Show further that this solution is periodic if the function $f(t)$ is periodic.

180.* Suppose $a(t) \geq c > 0$, and $f(t) \to 0$ for $t \to +\infty$. Show that every solution of the equation

$$\frac{dx}{dt} + a(t)\, x = f(t)$$

approaches 0 for $t \to +\infty$.

181.* In the same equation suppose that $a(t) \geq c > 0$, and let $x_o(t)$ be the solution for which the initial condition $x_o(0) = b$ is satisfied. Show that for every positive $\epsilon > 0$ there is a $\delta > 0$, such that if we perturb the function $f(t)$ and the number b by a quantity less than δ then the solution $x_o(t)$, $t \geq 0$, is perturbed by less than ϵ. The word perturbed is understood in the following sense : $f(t)$ is replaced by $f_1(t)$, and b is replaced by b_1 where

$$\left| f_1(t) - f(t) \right| < \delta \, , \quad \left| b_1 - b \right| < \delta \, .$$

This property of the solution $x_o(t)$ is called <u>stability for persistent disturbances</u>.

182.* Let a be a positive constant, $a > 0$, and let $f(x) \to b$ for $x \to 0$. Show that exactly one solution of the equation

$$xy' + ay = f(x)$$

is bounded for $x \to 0$, and find the limit of this solution for $x \to 0$.

183.* Consider the same problem but with a a negative constant: $a < 0$. Show that every solution of the equation now has a limit, that all limits are the same as $x \to 0$. Find the value of the limit.

184.* Find a periodic solution of the equation

$$y' = y \cos^2 x + \sin x .$$

Express the solution as a definite integral.

185.* Show that only one solution of the equation

$$xy' - (2x^2 + 1) y = x^2$$

has a finite limit for $x \to + \infty$, and give the value of this limit. Express the solution as an integral.

EXACT EQUATIONS

Integrating Factors

The equation

$$M(x,y) \; dx + N \; (x,y) \; dy = 0 \tag{1}$$

is called exact if the left member is the total differential

of some function $F(x,y)$. This will occur if $\partial M/\partial y \equiv \partial N/\partial x$.

A convenient way to solve this equation is to find a function

$F(x,y)$ which has a total differential $dF(x,y) = F_x \, dx + F_y \, dy$

equal to the left member of the equation (1). Having found this

function, the general solution of equation (1) is clearly

$F(x,y) = C$, where C is an arbitrary constant.

Example. Solve the equation

$$(2x + 3x^2 y) \; dx + (x^3 - 3y^2) \; dy = 0. \tag{2}$$

Since $\partial (2x + 3x^2 y) / \partial y = 3x^2, \partial (x^3 - 3y^2)/\partial x = 3x^2$,

equation (2) is exact. We must find a function $F(x,y)$ that

has a total differential $dF = F_x \, dx + F_y \, dy$, equal to the

left member of the equation (2).

Therefore

$$F_x = 2x + 3x^2y, \quad F_y = x^3 - 3y^2. \tag{3}$$

If the first of these relations is integrated with respect to x considering y to be a constant, we obtain

$$F = \int (2x + 3x^2y) \, dx = x^2 + x^3y + \phi(y),$$

where the last term is an unknown function of y. But the partial derivative of F with respect to y is given by the second equation (3) and from this we obtain the following

$$(x^2 + x^3y + \phi(y))_y = x^3 - 3y^2; \quad \phi'(y) = -3y^2;$$

$$\phi(y) = -y^3 + \text{const.}$$

Therefore we obtain $F(x,y) = x^2 + x^3y - y^3$, and the general solution of equation (2) has the form

$$x^2 + x^3y - y^3 = C.$$

By an integrating factor of the equation

$$M(x,y) \, dx + N(x,y) \, dy = 0 \tag{4}$$

is meant a function $m(x,y) \neq 0$, so that the equation that results when (4) is multiplied through by the function $m(x,y)$ becomes exact. Thus an integrating factor must satisfy the relation

$$(mM)_y = (mN)_x \tag{5}$$

If M or N of equation (4) have continuous partial derivatives,
and these functions are not identically 0, an integrating factor always exists. On the other hand, there is no general
method for obtaining such a factor. There are recipes that
are available in certain cases, as follows.

(i) If $z = \phi(x,y)$ is a preassigned function of x and
y, for example $z = x$, $z = y$, $z = xy$, $z = x/y$, it can be
determined whether an integrating factor exists that depends
only on z; and if one does exist, it can be found. To see
this, set $m = m(z)$ in relation (5). If the result of this
substitution yields an equation that can be written in the form

$$G(m, m_z, z) = 0, \tag{6}$$

then an integrating factor depending on z alone exists and it
can be found by solving equation (6).

Consider the equation

$$(y^4 - 4xy)dx + (2xy^3 - 3x^2) \, dy = 0. \tag{7}$$

Is there an integrating factor depending only on $z = xy$?

This question is answered by substituting $m = m(z)$ in
the differential condition (5):

$$[m \, (y^4 - 4xy)]_y = [m \, (2xy^3 - 3x^2)]_x$$

Since $m_x = m_z \cdot z_x = m_z \cdot y$, $m_y = m_z \cdot z_y = m_z \cdot x$, then the condition above amounts to the following

$$m_z \cdot xy \, (y^3 + x) = m \cdot 2(y^3 + x).$$

If we replace xy by z, and cancel the factor $y^3 + x$, we see that the equation to be solved is

$$z \, m_z = 2m. \tag{8}$$

Since the letters x,y do not appear explicitly in this equation, an integrating factor exists which depends only on z. From equation (8) we find the result $m = Cz^2$. But the constant C is arbitrary and can be taken to be 1. Thus $m = x^2 y^2$ is an integrating factor for equation (7).

If equation (4) can be written in the form

$$d \, \phi(x,y) + M_1(x,y) \, dx + N_1(x,y) \, dy = 0, \tag{9}$$

where $d \, \phi(x,y)$ is the total differential of some function $\phi(x,y)$ then the equation can be solved if we can find, according to the recipe above, an integrating factor for the subsidiary equation $M_1(x,y) \, dx + N_1(x,y) \, dy = 0$, that is a function of z alone $[z = \phi(x,y)]$. If such an integrating factor exists, then it is also an integrating factor for equation (9).

Example. Consider the equation

$$(xy + y^4) \, dx + (x^2 - xy^3) \, dy = 0.$$

If we collect the terms according to degree, we obtain

$$x(y \, dx + x \, dy) + y^3 (y \, dx - x \, dy) = 0.$$

Now we divide by x and obtain the equation

$$d \, (xy) + \frac{y^3}{x} (y \, dx - x \, dy) = 0, \tag{10}$$

in which the first term is a total differential. The subsidiary equation is

$$\frac{y^3}{x} (y \, dx - x \, dy) = 0 \tag{11}$$

and has an integrating factor depending only on z = xy, as the above method shows. This factor is m = $1/z^2$.

Now we multiply the entire equation (10) by this integrating factor and obtain the equation

$$\frac{d(xy)}{x^2 y^2} + \frac{y^2}{x^3} \, dx - \frac{y}{x^2} \, dy = 0,$$

in which the left member is a total differential.

Sometimes parts of equation (4) can be recognized as total differentials of a function $\phi(x,y)$. In such a case the equation may be simplified by introducing new variables (x,z) or (y,z) in place of the variables (x,y). Here z equals $\phi(x,y)$.

In special cases it is even desirable to change the variables from (x,y) to (u,v), where $u = \phi(x,y)$ and
$v = \psi(x,y)$.

Example. We consider equation (10) from this point of
view. Since $y\,dx - x\,dy = y^2\,d\,(x/y)$, the equation (10) can
be written in the form

$$d\,(xy) + \frac{y^5}{x}\,d\,(x/y) = 0.$$

We now write $xy = u$, $x/y = v$, and the equation takes the form
$du + u^2 dv/v^3 = 0$, which is easily solved since the variables
are separable.

Note that if an exact equation has solution $F = C$, then
any function of F is an integrating factor. If

$$Mdx + Ndy$$

has integrating factor $\phi(z)$ and solution $F = C$, then
$\psi(F)\,\phi(z)$ is an integrating factor, where ψ is an arbitrary
differentiable function.

In problems 186-194, check that the differential equations are exact and solve each equation.

186. $2xy\,dx + (x^2 - y^2)\,dy = 0.$

187. $(2 - 9xy^2)\,x\,dx + (4y^2 - 6x^3)\,y\,dy = 0.$

188. $e^{-y}\,dx - (2y + xe^{-y})\,dy = 0.$

189. $\frac{y}{x}\,dx + (y^3 + \ln x)\,dy = 0.$

190. $\frac{3x^2 + y^2}{y^2}\,dx - \frac{2x^3 + 5y}{y^3}\,dy = 0.$

191. $2x\left(1 + \sqrt{x^2 - y}\right)dx - \sqrt{x^2 - y}\,dy = 0.$

192. $(1 + y^2 \sin 2x)\,dx - 2y \cos^2 x\,dy = 0.$

193. $3x^2(1 + \ln y)\,dx = \left(2y - \frac{x^3}{y}\right)dy.$

194. $\left(\frac{x}{\sin y} + 2\right)dx + \frac{(x^2 + 1)\cos y}{\cos 2y - 1}\,dy = 0.$

Solve equations 195-220 by finding an integrating factor of suitable form, or by making a suitable change of variables.

195. $(x^2 + y^2 + x)\,dx + y\,dy = 0.$

196. $(x^2 + y^2 + y)\,dx - x\,dy = 0.$

197. $x\,dx = (x\,dy + y\,dx)\sqrt{1 + x^2}.$

198. $xy^2(xy' + y) = 1.$

199. $y^2\,dx - (xy + x^3)\,dy = 0.$

200. $\left(y - \frac{1}{x}\right)dx + \frac{dy}{y} = 0.$

201. $(x^2 + 3\ln y)\,y\,dx = x\,dy.$

202. $y^2\,dx + (xy + \operatorname{tg} xy)\,dy = 0.$

203. $y(x + y)\,dx + (xy + 1)\,dy = 0.$

204. $y(y^2 + 1)\,dx + x(y^2 - x + 1)\,dy = 0.$

205. $(x^2 + 2x + y)\,dx = (x - 3x^2y)\,dy.$

206. $y\,dx - x\,dy = 2x^3 \operatorname{tg} \frac{y}{x}\,dx.$

207. $y^2\,dx + (e^x - y)\,dy = 0.$

208. $xy\,dx = (y^3 + x^2y + x^2)\,dy.$

209. $x^2y(y\,dx + x\,dy) = 2y\,dx + x\,dy.$

210. $(x^2 - y^2 + y)\,dx + x(2y - 1)\,dy = 0.$

211. $(2x^2y^2 + y)\,dx + (x^3y - x)\,dy = 0.$

212. $(2x^2y^3 - 1)\,y\,dx + (4x^2y^3 - 1)\,x\,dy = 0.$

213. $y(x + y^2)\,dx + x^2(y - 1)\,dy = 0.$

214. $(x^2 - \sin^2 y)\,dx + x \sin 2y\,dy = 0.$

215. $x(\ln y + 2\ln x - 1)\,dy = 2y\,dx.$

216. $(x^2 + 1)(2x\,dx + \cos y\,dy) = 2x \sin y\,dx.$

217. $(2x^3y^2 - y)\,dx + (2x^2y^3 - x)\,dy = 0.$

218. $x^2y^3 + y + (x^3y^2 - x)\,y' = 0.$

219. $(x^2 - y)\,dx + x(y + 1)\,dy = 0.$

220. $y^2(y\,dx - 2x\,dy) = x^3(x\,dy - 2y\,dx).$

Section 7

QUESTIONS ON EXISTENCE AND UNIQUENESS OF SOLUTIONS

A differential equation, particularly a differential equation of first order, is easily rewritten as an integral equation. In this manner a solution with given initial conditions can be found by the method of successive approximations.

Estimate the length of the interval on which Picard's theorem guarantees the existence of a solution and the convergence of his method of successive approximations [Coddington-Levinson, p. 6, (1.6)]

221. $y' = x - y^2$, $y(0)$. Find y_0, y_1, y_2, y_3.

222. $y' = y^2 - 3x^2 - 1$, $y(0) = 1$. Find y_0, y_1, y_2.

223. $y' = y + e^y$, $y(0) = 1$. Find y_0, y_1, y_2.

224.* Estimate the error of the approximation y_3 in problem 221 for $x = 0.5$ and for $x = 1$.

Hint. Calculate the remainder of the series that is used to prove the existence of a solution.

225.* Show that the solution of the equation $y' = x^3 - y^3$ with arbitrary initial value $y(x_0) = y_0$ exists for all x, $x_0 \leq x < \infty$.

42

In problems 226-240 state a theorem which guarantees the
uniqueness of the solution of the equation in question. Be
sure that the example satisfies the hypotheses of the theorem.
In problems 229 and 230 the right member of the equation is
defined at y = 0 by the specification that it be continuous.

226. $y' = 2xy + y^2.$
227. $y' = 3\sqrt[3]{y^2}.$
228. $y' = 3\sqrt[3]{y^2} + 1.$
229. $y' = y \ln y.$
230. $y' = y \ln^2 y.$
231. $y' = \sqrt[3]{y} + x.$

232. $y' = \dfrac{y+2}{x+y}.$
233. $y' = \dfrac{x+2y-4}{x-y-1}.$
234. $y' = \operatorname{tg} y + 1.$
235. $y' = \sqrt{\sin y}.$
236. $y' = 2 + \sqrt[3]{y - 2x}.$
237. $y' = \sqrt{x+2y} - x.$
238. $y' = \sin x + \cos y.$
239. $y' = \dfrac{\sqrt{y}-x}{x-2}.$
240. $xy' = y + \sqrt{y^2 - x^2}.$

EQUATIONS IN WHICH THE DERIVATIVE APPEARS IMPLICITLY

An equation of the form $F(x,y,y') = 0$ can be solved in the following manner.

If it is possible to solve the equation $F(x,y,y') = 0$ explicitly for y' in terms of x and y, the problem is re-written in the form $y' = f(x,y)$. This equation must then be solved. In some cases more than one equation $y' = f(x,y)$ is obtained from the given equation. In this case each equation must be solved and the corresponding solutions checked in the original equation.

A method called parametric solution proceeds as follows. (We explain a simple variant of a method described more generally in standard texts.)

The first step is to solve the equation $F(x,y,y') = 0$ for y, obtaining a result of the form $y = f(x,y')$. If we introduce the parameter

$$p = \frac{dy}{dx} = y',$$
(1)

we obtain

$$y = f(x,p). \tag{2}$$

Now we take the total derivative of equation (2), replace dy by p dx (see (1)), and obtain an equation of the form

$$M(x,p) \, dx + N \, (x,p) \, dp = 0.$$

If this equation can be solved in the form $x = \phi(p)$, the original equation is solved in parametric form by use of equation (2): $x = \phi(p)$, $y = f(\phi(p), p)$.

The equation $x = f(y,y')$ can be solved in the same manner.

This method is to be used in problems 267-286 below.

A solution $y = \phi(x)$ of the equation $F(x,y,y') = 0$ is called singular, if every point of this curve has the property that a second solution of the differential equation passes through this point, that is, has the same slope as the solution $y = \phi(x)$, and yet the second solution is different from the singular solution in every neighborhood of the given point. (The term singular solution is used in other senses by certain authors.)

If the function $F(x,y,y')$ and its partial derivatives

$\partial F/\partial y$, $\partial F/\partial y'$ are continuous, then every singular solution

of the equation

$$F(x,y,y') = 0 \qquad\qquad (3)$$

also satisfies the condition

$$\frac{\partial F(x,y,y')}{\partial y'} = 0. \qquad\qquad (4)$$

Thus the singular solutions of equation (3) are obtained by

eliminating y' from equations (3), (4). The equation

$\psi(x,y) = 0$ obtained in this elimination is called the dis-

criminant of the original differential equation. It is neces-

sary to check each branch of the discriminant curve to find if

it is a valid solution of equation (3). If such is the case

then it can be checked further whether it is a singular solu-

tion, that is, whether more than one integral curve passes

through each of its points. This last property is easily

checked whenever the complete or general solution of the equa-

tion is known.

If a family of curves $\vartheta(x,y,C) = 0$ has an <u>envelope</u>

$y = \phi(x)$,   and if the family satisfies the equation $F(x,y,y')$

$= 0$, then the <u>envelope</u> will be a singular solution of the equation. If the function ϑ has continuous derivatives with respect to C, a necessary condition for the existence of an envelope is that the relations

$$\vartheta(x,y,C) = 0, \qquad \frac{\partial \vartheta (x,y,C)}{\partial C} = 0$$

hold. Thus, one can check whether the curve obtained by eliminating these two curves is indeed an envelope of the given family.

In problems 241-250 find all solutions of the given equations; indicate the singular solutions if there are any; draw pictures.

241. $y'^2 - y^2 = 0$.

242. $8y'^3 = 27y$.

243. $(y' + 1)^3 = 27(x+y)^2$.

244. $y^2(y'^2 + 1) = 1$.

245. $y'^2 - 4y^3 = 0$.

246. $y'^2 = 4y^3(1 - y)$.

247. $xy'^2 = y$.

248. $yy'^3 + x = 1$.

249. $y'^3 + y^2 = yy'(y'+1)$.

250. $4(1-y) = (3y-2)^2 \, y'^2$.

Solve equations 251-266 for y' and then find the solution by the usual methods. Indicate the singular solutions if there are any.

251. $y'^2 + xy = y^2 + xy'$.

252. $xy'(xy' + y) = 2y^2$.

253. $xy'^2 - 2yy' + x = 0$.

254. $xy'^2 = y(2y' - 1)$.

255. $y'^2 + x = 2y$.

256. $y'^3 + (x + 2)\,e^y = 0$.

257. $y'^2 - 2xy' = 8x^2$.

258. $(xy' + 3y)^2 = 7x$.

259. $y'^2 - 2yy' = y^2(e^x - 1)$.

260. $y'(2y - y') = y^2 \sin^2 x$.

261. $y'^4 + y^2 = y^4$.

262. $x(y - xy')^2 = xy'^2 - 2yy'$.

263. $y(xy' - y)^2 = y - 2xy'$.

264. $yy'(yy' - 2x) = x^2 - 2y^2$.

265. $y'^2 + 4xy' - y^2 - 2x^2y = x^4 - 4x^2$.

266. $y(y - 2xy')^2 = 2y'$.

Solve equations 267-286 in parametric form.

267. $x = y'^3 + y'$.

268. $x(y'^2 - 1) = 2y'$.

269. $x = y' \sqrt{y'^2 + 1}$.

270. $y'(x - \ln y') = 1$.

271. $y = y'^2 + 2y'^3$.

272. $y = \ln(1 + y'^2)$.

273. $(y' + 1)^3 = (y' - y)^2$.

274. $y = (y' - 1)e^{y'}$.

275. $y'^4 - y'^2 = y^2$.

276. $y'^2 - y'^3 = y^2$.

277. $y'^4 = 2yy' + y^2$.

278. $y'^2 - 2xy' = x^2 - 4y$.

279. $5y + y'^2 = x(x + y')$.

280. $x^2 y'^2 = xyy' + 1$.

281. $y'^3 + y^2 = xyy'$.

282. $2xy' - y = y' \ln yy'$.

283. $y' = e^{\frac{xy'}{y}}$.

284. $y = xy' - x^2 y'^3$.

285. $y = 2xy' + y^2 y'^3$.

286. $y(y - 2xy')^3 = y'^2$.

Equations 287-297 are of the Lagrange-Clairaut type.

287. $y = xy' - y'^2$.

288. $y + xy' = 4\sqrt{y'}$.

289. $y = 3xy' - 7y'^3$.

290. $y = xy' - (2 + y')$.

291. $x(y'^2 + 1) = 2yy'$.

292. $y = xy'^2 - 2y'^3$.

293. $xy' - y = \ln y'$.

294. $xy'(y' + 2) = y$.

295. $2y'^2(y - xy') = 1$.

296. $2xy' - y = \ln y'$.

297. $y'^3 = 3(xy' - y)$.

298. Find a curve such that its tangent cuts off a triangle of area $2a^2$ on the coordinate axes.

299. Find a curve such that the sum of the squares of the reciprocals of the lengths of the segments cut by its tangent from the coordinate axes is 1.

300. Find a curve that goes through the origin, and is so arranged that the segments of the normal cut off in the first quadrant, has a constant length equal to 2.

Section 9

MISCELLANEOUS FIRST ORDER EQUATIONS

Solve equations 301-330 and draw a graph of the solutions.

All problems in this section use methods introduced earlier.

301. $xy' + x^2 + xy - y = 0.$ 302. $2xy' + y^2 = 1.$

303. $(2xy^2 - y)\,dx + x\,dy = 0.$

304. $(xy' + y)^2 = x^2 y'.$ 305. $y - y' = y^2 + xy'.$

306. $(x + 2y^3)\,y' = y.$ 307. $y'^3 - y' e^{2x} = 0.$

308. $x^2 y' = y(x + y).$ 309. $(1 - x^2)\,dy + xy\,dx = 0.$

310. $y'^2 + 2(x - 1)\,y' - 2y = 0.$

311. $y + y' \ln^2 y = (x + 2 \ln y)\,y'.$

312. $x^2 y' - 2xy = 3y.$ 313. $x + yy' = y^2 \left(1 + y'^2\right).$

314. $y = (xy' + 2y)^2.$ 315. $y' = \dfrac{1}{x - y^2}.$

316. $y'^3 + (3x - 6)\,y' = 3y.$ 317. $x - \dfrac{y}{y'} = \dfrac{2}{y}.$

318. $2y'^3 - 3y'^2 + x = y.$ 319. $(x + y)^2\,y' = 1.$

320. $2x^3 yy' + 3x^2 y^2 + 7 = 0.$ 321. $\dfrac{dx}{x} = \left(\dfrac{1}{y} - 2x\right) dy.$

322. $xy' = e^y + 2y'.$ 323. $2(x - y^2)\,dy = y\,dx.$

324. $x^2 y'^2 + y^2 = 2x(2 - yy').$

325. $dy + (xy - xy^3)\,dx = 0.$ 326. $2x^2 y' = y^2 (2xy' - y).$

327. $\dfrac{y - xy'}{x + yy'} = 2.$ 328. $x(x - 1)\,y' + 2xy = 1.$

329. $xy(xy' - y)^2 + 2y' = 0.$ 330. $(1 - x^2)\,y' - 2xy^2 = xy.$

Solve equations 331-420.

331. $y' + y = xy^3$.

332. $(xy^2 - x)\,dx + (y + xy)\,dy = 0$.

333. $(\sin x + y)\,dy + (y\cos x - x^2)\,dx = 0$.

334. $3y'^3 - xy' + 1 = 0$. **335.** $yy' + y^2\operatorname{ctg} x = \cos x$.

336. $(e^y + 2xy)\,dx + (e^y + x)\,x\,dy = 0$.

337. $xy'^2 = y - y'$. **338.** $x(x+1)(y'-1) = y$.

339. $y(y - xy') = \sqrt{x^4 + y^4}$. **340.** $xy' + y = \ln y'$.

341. $x^2(dy - dx) = (x + y)\,y\,dx$.

342. $y' + x\sqrt[3]{v} = 3v$. **343.** $(x\cos y + \sin 2v)\,v' = 1$.

344. $y'^2 - yy' + e^x = 0$. **345.** $y' = \dfrac{x}{y}\,e^{2x} + y$.

346. $(xy' - y)^3 = y'^3 - 1$. **347.** $(4xy - 3)\,y' + y^2 = 1$.

348. $y'\sqrt{x} = \sqrt{y - x} + \sqrt{x}$. **349.** $xy' = 2\sqrt{y}\cos x - 2y$.

350. $3y'^4 = y' + y$. **351.** $y^2(y - xy') = x^3y'$.

352. $y' = (4x + y - 3)^2$.

353. $(\cos x - x\sin x)\,y\,dx + (x\cos x - 2y)\,dy = 0$.

354. $x^2y'^2 - 2xyy' = x^2 + 3y^2$.

355. $\dfrac{xy'}{y} + 2xy\ln x + 1 = 0$. **356.** $xy' = x\sqrt{y - x^2} + 2y$.

357. $(1 - x^2y)\,dx + x^2(y - x)\,dy = 0$.

358. $(2xe^y + y^4)\,y' = ye^y$. **359.** $xy'(\ln y - \ln x) = y$.

360. $2y' = x + \ln y'$.

361. $(2x^2y - 3y^2)\,y' = 6x^2 - 2xy^2 + 1$.

362. $yy' = 4x + 3y - 2$.

363. $y^2y' + x^2\sin^3 x = y^3\operatorname{ctg} x$.

364. $2xy' - y = \sin y'$.

365. $(x^2y^2 + 1)\,y + (xy - 1)^2\,xy' = 0$.

366. $y\sin x + y'\cos x = 1$.

367. $x\,dy - y\,dx = x\sqrt{x^2 + y^2}\,dx$.

368. $y^2 + x^2y'^5 = xy(y'^2 + y'^3)$.

369. $y' = \sqrt[3]{2x - y} + 2$.

370. $\left(x - y\cos\dfrac{y}{x}\right)dx + x\cos\dfrac{y}{x}\,dy = 0$.

371. $2\left(x^2y + \sqrt{1 + x^4y^2}\right)dx + x^3\,dy = 0$.

372. $\left(y' - x\sqrt{y}\right)(x^2 - 1) = xy$.

373. $y'^3 + (y'^2 - 2y')\,x = 3y' - y$.

374. $(2x + 3y - 1)\,dx + (4x + 6y - 5)\,dy = 0$.

375. $(2xy^2 - y)\,dx + (y^2 + x + y)\,dy = 0$.

376. $y = y'\sqrt{1 + y'^2}$. **377.** $y^2 = (xyy' + 1)\ln x$.

378. $4y = x^2 + y'^2$.

379. $2x\,dy + y\,dx + xy^2(x\,dy + y\,dx) = 0$.

380. $x\,dx + (x^2\operatorname{ctg} y - 3\cos y)\,dy = 0$.

381. $x^2 y'^2 - 2(xy - 2)y' + y^2 = 0.$

382. $xy' + 1 = e^{x-y}.$ **383.** $y' = \operatorname{tg}(y - 2x).$

384. $3x^2 - y = y' \sqrt{x^2 + 1}.$ **385.** $yy' + xy = x^3.$

386. $x(x-1)y' + y^3 = xy.$ **387.** $xy' = 2y + \sqrt{1 + y'^2}.$

388. $(2x + y + 5)y' = 3x + 6.$ **389.** $y' + \operatorname{tg} y = x \sec y.$

390. $y'^4 = 4y(xy' - 2y)^2.$ **391.** $y' = \dfrac{y^2 - x}{2y(x+1)}.$

392. $xy' = x^2 e^{-y} + 2.$ **393.** $y' = 3x + \sqrt{y - x^2}.$

394. $x\,dy - 2y\,dx + xy^2(2x\,dy + y\,dx) = 0.$

395. $(x^3 - 2xy^2)\,dx + 3x^2 y\,dy = x\,dy - y\,dx.$

396. $(yy')^3 = 27x(y^2 - 2x^2).$ **397.** $y' - 8x\sqrt{y} = \dfrac{4xy}{x^2 - 1}.$

398. $[2x - \ln(y + 1)]\,dx - \dfrac{x+y}{y+1}\,dy = 0.$

399. $xy' = (x^2 + \operatorname{tg} y)\cos^2 y.$ **400.** $x^2(y - xy') = yy'^2.$

401. $y' = \dfrac{3x^2}{x^3 + y + 1}.$ **402.** $y' = \dfrac{(1+y)^2}{x(y+1) - x^2}.$

403. $(y - 2xy')^2 = 4yy'^3.$

404. $6x^5 y\,dx + (y^4 \ln y - 3x^6)\,dy = 0.$

405. $y' = \dfrac{1}{2}\sqrt{x} + \sqrt[3]{y}.$ **406.** $2xy' + 1 = y + \dfrac{x^2}{y-1}.$

407. $yy' + x = \dfrac{1}{2}\left(\dfrac{x^2 + y^2}{x}\right)^2.$ **408.** $y' = \left(\dfrac{3x + y^3 - 1}{y}\right)^2.$

409. $\left(x\sqrt{y^2 + 1} + 1\right)(y^2 + 1)\,dx = xy\,dy.$

410. $(x^2 + y^2 + 1)yy' + (x^2 + y^2 - 1)x = 0.$

411. $y^2(x - 1)\,dx = x(xy + x - 2y)\,dy.$

412. $(xy' - y)^2 = x^2 y^2 - x^4.$

413. $xyy' - x^2\sqrt{y^2 + 1} = (x + 1)(y^2 + 1).$

414. $(x^2 - 1)y' + y^2 - 2xy + 1 = 0.$

415. $y' \operatorname{tg} y + 4x^3 \cos y = 2x.$

416. $(xy' - y)^2 = y'^2 - \dfrac{2yy'}{x} + 1.$

417. $(x + y)(1 - xy)\,dx + (x + 2y)\,dy = 0.$

418. $(3xy + x + y)y\,dx + (4xy + x + 2y)x\,dy = 0.$

419. $(x^2 - 1)\,dx + (x^2 y^2 + x^3 + x)\,dy = 0.$

420. $x\left(y'^2 + e^{2y}\right) = -2y'.$

Section 10

EQUATIONS WHICH CAN BE REDUCED TO
EQUATIONS OF LOWER ORDER

If a differential equation does not involve the dependent
variable y explicitly, the order of the equation can be de-
pressed by introducing a new dependent variable. In particular
the equation

$$F(x, y^{(k)}, y^{(k+1)}, \ldots, y^{(n)}) = 0$$

can be written as an equation of order $n - k$ by introducing
the new variable $y^{(k)} = z$.

If a differential equation does not involve the independent
variable x explicitly, the order can be reduced by rewriting
the equation so that the dependent variable y becomes the
independent variable. Thus if the original equation is

$$F(y, y', y'', \ldots, y^{(n)}) = 0,$$

the equation is rewritten by using the device

$$y' = p(y),$$

where $p(y)$ is an unknown function of y.

<u>Example</u>. Solve the equation $2yy'' = y'^2 + 1$.

Solution. Since x does not appear explicitly, the device $y' = p(y)$ avails. Thus

$$y'' = \frac{d(y')}{dx} = \frac{dp(y)}{dx} = \frac{dp}{dy} \cdot \frac{dy}{dx} = p'p.$$

From $y' = p$, we obtained $y'' = pp'$, and the equation becomes

$$2ypp' = p^2 + 1.$$

This equation has lower order than did the original equation. Its solution is $p = \pm\sqrt{Cy - 1}$. From this, $y' = \pm\sqrt{Cy - 1}$. Solving the latter, we obtain

$$4(Cy - 1) = C^2(x + C_2).$$

If a differential equation is homogeneous in the symbols $y, y', y'', \ldots$, i.e. if the equation is unaltered when these symbols are replaced by $ky, ky', ky'', \cdots$, the order of the equation can be reduced by taking $y' = yz$, where z is a new unknown function.

The order of an equation can be reduced if it is homogeneous (in the extended sense) in the variables x, y. This means that the equation is not changed if x is replaced by kx, y by $k^m y$, y' by $k^{m-1} y'$, y'' by $k^{m-2} y''$, etc. The possibility of finding m depends on the possibility of satis-

fying a set of simultaneous conditions which state that the

degree of homogeneity of each term must be the same. Thus, the

equation

$$2 x^4 y'' - 3 y^2 = x^4$$

is homogeneous in the extended sense if the degrees

$$4 + (m - 2), \quad 2m, \quad 4$$

of the three terms can be made the same. This does occur for

$m = 2$.

Having obtained the value of m (if it exists) one

introduces the new variable $z = z(t)$ by the relations

$$x = e^t, \quad y = ze^{mt}$$

In the new equation, the variable t does not appear explicitly.

Thus its order can be reduced.

Thus for example,

$$dy/dx = e^{-t} dy/dt, \quad d^2 y/dx^2 = e^{-t} d/dt (e^{-t} dy/dt).$$

The order of an equation can be reduced if the equation

can be written so that each member is a polynomial in the

derivative y', or of some function of y'. For example, on

division by y y', the equation $y y'' = y'^2$ becomes

$$\frac{y''}{y'} = \frac{y'}{y}; \quad (\ln y')' = (\ln y)'; \quad \ln y' = \ln y + \ln C; \quad y' = yC.$$

and the last equation has lower order.

Solve equations 421-450.

421. $x^2 y'' = y'^2$.

422. $2xy'y'' = y'^2 - 1$.

423. $y^3 y'' = 1$.

424. $y'^2 + 2yy'' = 0$.

425. $y'' = 2yy'$.

426. $yy'' + 1 = y'^2$.

427. $y''(e^x + 1) + y' = 0$.

428. $y''' = y''^2$.

429. $yy'' = y'^2 - y'^3$.

430. $y''' = 2(y'' - 1)\operatorname{ctg} x$.

431. $2yy'' = y^2 + y'^2$.

432. $y''^3 + xy'' = 2y'$.

433. $y''^2 + y' = xy''$.

434. $y'' + y'^2 = 2e^{-y}$.

435. $x^2 y''' = y''^2$.

436. $y''^2 = y'^2 + 1$.

437. $y'' = e^y$.

438. $y'' - xy''' + y'''^3 = 0$

439. $2y'(y'' + 2) = xy''^2$.

440. $y^4 - y^3 y'' = 1$.

441. $y'^2 = (3y - 2y')y''$.

442. $y''(2y' + x) = 1$.

443. $y''^2 - 2y'y''' + 1 = 0$.

444. $(1 - x^2)y'' + xy' = 2$.

445. $yy'' - 2yy' \ln y = y'^2$.

446. $(y' + 2y)y'' = y'^2$.

447. $xy'' = y' + x \sin \dfrac{y'}{x}$.

448. $y'''y'^2 = y''^3$.

449. $yy'' + y = y'^2$.

450. $xy'' = y' + x(y'^2 + x^2)$.

Solve equations 451-454. Use integration by parts to reduce any iterated integral to a single integration. For example,

$$\int_0^x \int_0^s \frac{\sin t}{t}\, dt\, ds$$

$$= s \int_0^s \frac{\sin t}{t}\, dt \Bigg]_0^x - \int_0^x \sin s\, ds$$

451. $xy^{\mathrm{IV}} = 1$.

452. $xy'' = \sin x$.

453. $y''' = 2xy''$

454. $xy^{\mathrm{IV}} + y''' = e^x$.

Solve equations 455-462 by rewriting so that each member becomes a polynomial in the derivative y' (or something similar).

455. $yy''' = y'y''.$

456. $y'y''' = 2y''^2.$

457. $yy'' = y'(y'+1).$

458. $5y'''^2 - 3y''y^{IV} = 0.$

459. $yy'' + y'^2 = 1.$

460. $y'' = xy' + y + 1.$

461. $xy'' = 2yy' - y'$

462. $xy'' - y' = x^2yy'.$

In problems 463-480, reduce the order of the given equation by noting that it is homogeneous. Solve the equation.

463. $xyy'' - xy'^2 = yy'.$

464. $yy'' = y'^2 + 15y^2\sqrt{x}.$

465. $(x^2 + 1)\left(y'^2 - yy''\right) = xyy'.$

466. $xyy'' + xy'^2 = 2yy'.$

467. $x^2yy'' = (y - xy')^2.$

468. $y'' + \dfrac{y'}{x} + \dfrac{y}{x^2} = \dfrac{y'^2}{y}.$

469. $y(xy'' + y') = xy'^2(1-x).$

470. $x^2yy'' + y'^2 = 0.$

471. $x^2\left(y'^2 - 2yy''\right) = y^2.$

472. $xyy'' = y'(y + y').$

473. $4x^2y^3y'' = x^2 - y^4.$

474. $x^3y'' = (y - xy')(y - xy' - x).$

475. $\dfrac{y^2}{x^2} + y'^2 = 3xy'' + \dfrac{2yy'}{x}.$

476. $y'' = \left(2xy - \dfrac{5}{x}\right)y' + 4y^2 - \dfrac{4y}{x^2}.$

477. $x^2\left(2yy'' - y'^2\right) = 1 - 2xyy'.$

478. $x^2\left(yy'' - y'^2\right) + xyy' = (2xy' - 3y)\sqrt{x^3}.$

479. $x^4\left(y'^2 - 2yy''\right) = 4x^3yy' + 1.$

480. $yy' + xyy'' - xy'^2 = x^3.$

In problems 481-500, reduce the order of the given equation to first order.

481. $y''\left(3+yy'^2\right)=y'^4.$ **482.** $y''^2-y'y'''=\left(\dfrac{y'}{x}\right)^2.$

483. $yy'+2x^2y''=xy'^2.$ **484.** $y'^2+2xyy''=0.$

485. $2xy^2(xy''+y')+1=0.$ **486.** $x\left(y''+y'^2\right)=y'^2+y'.$

487. $y^2\left(y'y'''-2y''^2\right)=y'^4.$ **488.** $y(2xy''+y')=xy'^2+1.$

489. $y''+2yy'^2=\left(2x+\dfrac{1}{x}\right)y'.$

490. $y'y'''=y''^2+y'^2y''.$ **491.** $yy''=y'^2+2xy^2.$

492. $y'^4=y'^5-yy'^3y''.$ **493.** $2yy'''=y'.$

494. $y'''y'^2=1.$ **495.** $y^2y'''=y'^3.$

496. $x^2yy''+1=(1-y)xy'.$

497. $y^2\left(x^3y'''-2xy'-3y\right)=x^3y'\left(3yy''-2y'^2\right).$

498. $\left(y'y'''-3y''^2\right)y=y'^5.$

499. $y^2\left(y'y'''-2y''^2\right)=yy'^2y''+2y'^4.$

500. $x^2\left(y^2y'''-y'^3\right)=2y^2y'-3xyy'^2.$

In problems 501-505, find the solution (or solutions) that satisfy the given conditions.

501. $yy''=2xy'^2;$ $y(2)=2,$ $y'(2)=0,5.$

502. $2y'''-3y'^2=0;$ $y(0)=-3,$ $y'(0)=1,$ $y''(0)=-1.$

503. $x^2y''-3xy'=\dfrac{6y^2}{x^2}-4y;$ $y(1)=1,$ $y'(1)=4.$

504. $y'''=3yy';$ $y(0)=-2,$ $y'(0)=0,$ $y''(0)=4,5.$

505. $y''\cos y+y'^2\sin y=y';$ $y(-1)=\dfrac{\pi}{6},$ $y'(-1)=2.$

506. Find a curve such that the radius of curvature at an arbitrary point is twice the length of the segment of the normal drawn from this point to the axis of abscissas. Consider two cases: (a) the curve is convex to the axis of abscissas; (b) the curve is concave.

507. Find a curve in which the radius of curvature at an arbitrary point is inversely proportional to the cosine of the angle between the tangent line and the axis of abscissas.

508. Find the shape of a uniform inextensible filament fastened at both ends, if the filament supports a load such that the horizontal projection of the load supported by each unit of length is constant (suspension bridge cable). Neglect the weight of the filament. Denote the load of the horizontal projection per unit length by p, and the horizontal component of the tension in the filament by T (a constant).

509. Find the shape of a uniform filament suspended under its own weight (fixed at both ends). Let q be the weight of a unit length of the filament, and set a = q/T, where T is defined in problem 508.

510. Show that the pendulum equation

$$y'' + \sin y = 0$$

has a particular solution y(x) that approaches π for

$x \to \infty$.

LINEAR EQUATIONS WITH CONSTANT COEFFICIENTS

We write $y' \equiv Dy$, $y'' \equiv D^2 y$, $y''' + y \equiv [D^3 + D]\, y$. The equations $y''' + y = 3x$, $y'' - 5y' + 6y = e^t \sin t$ with nonzero right-hand sides are <u>linear</u> but <u>not</u> <u>reduced</u>. The equation $[D^4 - 1]\, y = 0$ is <u>reduced</u> (also <u>homogeneous</u>). Study appendix A, in which we show that by solving an algebraic (polynomial) equation, all solutions of a <u>reduced</u> linear equation with constant coefficients can be written down. Appendix B outlines another method (Laplace transform).

Non-reduced equations can be solved by differentiating. To solve $[D^3 + 1]\, y = 3x$, note that $D^2 (3x) = 0$, so $D^2 [D^3 + 1]\, y = 0$. Every solution has the form

$$c_1 + c_2\, x + c_3\, e^{-x} + e^{-\frac{1}{2}x} (c_4 \cos \sqrt{3}\, x/2 + c_5 \sin \sqrt{3}\, x/2)$$

neglecting the last 3 terms for the moment, one finds

$$[D^3 + 1]\, (c_1 + c_2\, x) = c_1 + c_2\, x .$$

Thus $c_1 = 0$, $c_2 = 3$. To solve (1) $[D^2 - 5D + 6]\, y = e^t \sin t$, note that $[(D - 1)^2 + 1]\, (e^t \sin t) = 0$. The indicated terms are $e^t (c_1 \sin t + c_2 \cos t)$. Since $[D^2 - 5D + 6]\, (c_1 \sin t + c_2 \cos t)$

$$= 5\, (c_1 + c_2) \sin t + 5\, (-c_1 + c_2) \cos t, \quad \text{we have}$$

$$c_1 + c_2 = 1/5, \quad c_2 - c_1 = 0 .$$

Thus every solution of (1) has the form

$$y = \frac{1}{10} \ e^t \ (\sin t + \cos t) + c_3 \ e^{2t} + c_4 \ e^{3t} \quad .$$

As a last example, consider (2) $[(D - 1)^2 + 1] \ y = e^t \sin t$.

By differentiation, $[(D - 1)^2 + 1]^2 \ y = 0$. The indicated terms

are now $t \ e^t \ (c_1 \sin t + c_2 \cos t)$. Note that

$$[D - 1]^2 \ (e^t \ f) = e^t \ D^2 \ f.$$

Thus $\quad [(D - 1)^2 + 1] \ (t \ e^t (c_1 \sin t + c_2 \cos t))$

$= c_1 \ e^t \cos t - c_2 \ e^t \sin t;$ every solution of (2) has the form

$y = -t \ e^t \cos t + e^t \ (c_3 \sin t + c_4 \cos t)$.

Solve problems 511-548, using algebraic or Laplace transform

methods.

511. $y'' + y' - 2y = 0$.   512. $y'' + 4y' + 3y = 0$.
513. $y'' - 2y' = 0$.   514. $2y'' - 5y' + 2y = 0$.
515. $y'' - 4y' + 5y = 0$.   516. $y'' + 2y' + 10y = 0$.
517. $y'' + 4y = 0$.   518. $y''' - 8y = 0$.
519. $y^{IV} - y = 0$.   520. $y^{IV} + 4y = 0$.
521. $y^{VI} + 64y = 0$.   522. $y'' - 2y' + y = 0$.
523. $4y'' + 4y' + y = 0$.   524. $y^V - 6y^{IV} + 9y''' = 0$.
525. $y^V - 10y''' + 9y' = 0$.   526. $y^{IV} + 2y'' + y = 0$.
527. $y''' - 3y'' + 3y' - y = 0$.   528. $y''' - y'' - y' + y = 0$.
529. $y^{IV} - 5y'' + 4y = 0$ 530. $y^V + 8y''' + 16y' = 0$.
531. $y''' - 3y' + 2y = 0$.   532. $y^{IV} + 4y'' + 3y = 0$.
533. $y'' - 2y' - 3y = e^{4x}$.   534. $y'' + y = 4xe^x$.
535. $y'' - y = 2e^x - x^2$.   536. $y'' + y' - 2y = 3xe^x$.
537. $y'' - 3y' + 2y = \sin x$.   538. $y'' + y = 4 \sin x$.
539. $y'' - 5y' + 4y = 4x^2 e^{2x}$.   540. $y'' - 3y' + 2y = x \cos x$.
541. $y'' + 3y' - 4y = e^{-4x} + xe^{-x}$.
542. $y'' + 2y' - 3y = x^2 e^x$.
543. $y'' - 4y' + 8y = e^{2x} + \sin 2x$.
544. $y'' - 9y = e^{3x} \cos x$.   545. $y'' - 2y' + y = 6xe^x$.
546. $y'' + y = x \sin x$.   547. $y'' + 4y' + 4y = xe^{2x}$.
548. $y'' - 5y' = 3x^2 + \sin 5x$.

In problems 549-574, show the form of solution to look for (with undetermined coefficients).

549. $y'' - 2y' + 2y = e^x + x \cos x.$

550. $y'' + 6y' + 10y = 3xe^{-3x} - 2e^{3x} \cos x.$

551. $y'' - 8y' + 20y = 5xe^{4x} \sin 2x.$

552. $y'' + 7y' + 10y = xe^{-2x} \cos 5x.$

553. $y'' - 2y' + 5y = 2xe^x + e^x \sin 2x.$

554. $y'' - 2y' + y = 2xe^x + e^x \sin 2x.$

555. $y'' - 8y' + 17y = e^{4x}(x^2 - 3x \sin x).$

556. $y''' + y' = \sin x + x \cos x.$

557. $y''' - 2y'' + 4y' - 8y = e^{2x} \sin 2x + 2x^2.$

558. $y'' - 6y' + 8y = 5xe^{2x} + 2e^{4x} \sin x.$

559. $y'' + 2y' + y = x(e^{-x} - \cos x).$

560. $y''' - y'' - y' + y = 3e^x + 5x \sin x.$

561. $y'' - 6y' + 13y = x^2 e^{3x} - 3 \cos 2x.$

562. $y'' - 9y = e^{-3x}(x^2 + \sin 3x).$

563. $y^{IV} + y'' = 7x - 3 \cos x.$ **564.** $y'' + 4y = \cos x \cdot \cos 3x.$

565. $y''' - 4y'' + 3y' = x^2 + xe^{2x}.$

566. $y'' - 4y' + 5y = e^{2x} \sin^2 x.$

567. $y'' + 3y' + 2y = e^{-x} \cos^2 x.$

568. $y'' - 2y' + 2y = (x + e^x) \sin x.$

569. $y^{IV} + 5y'' + 4y = \sin x \cdot \cos 2x.$

570. $y'' - 3y' + 2y = 2^x.$ **571.** $y'' - y = 4 \operatorname{sh} x.$

572. $y'' + 4y' + 3y = \operatorname{ch} x.$ **573.** $y'' + 4y = \operatorname{sh} x \cdot \sin 2x.$

574. $y'' + 2y' + 2y = \operatorname{ch} x \cdot \sin x.$

Solve equations 575-580 by the method of variation of constants. That is, set up a general solution of the reduced equation, and replace the constants c_1, c_2 by appropriate functions of x.

575. $y'' - 2y' + y = \dfrac{e^x}{x}.$ **576.** $y'' + 3y' + 2y = \dfrac{1}{e^x + 1}.$

577. $y'' + y = \dfrac{1}{\sin x}.$ **578.** $y'' + 4y = 2 \operatorname{tg} x.$

579. $y'' + 2y' + y = 3e^{-x} \sqrt{x+1}.$

580*. $x^3(y'' - y) = x^2 - 2.$

Find the solutions of 581-588 that satisfy the given conditions.

581. $y''' - y' = 0$; $y(0) = 3$, $y'(0) = -1$, $y''(0) = 1$.
582. $y'' - 2y' + y = 0$; $y(2) = 1$, $y'(2) = -2$.
583. $y'' + y = 4e^x$; $y(0) = 4$, $y'(0) = -3$.
584. $y'' - 2y' = 2e^x$; $y(1) = -1$, $y'(1) = 0$.
585. $y'' - y = 2x$; $y(0) = 0$, $y(1) = -1$.
586. $y'' + y = 1$; $y(0) = 0$, $y\left(\dfrac{\pi}{2}\right) = 0$.
587. $y'' + y = 1$; $y(0) = 0$, $y(\pi) = 0$.
588. $y'' + y = 2x - \pi$; $y(0) = 0$, $y(\pi) = 0$.

In problems 589-600, solve the Euler equation. Solutions will have the form x^m, $(\ln x)^r x^m$, $x^m \cos(p \ln x)$, $(\ln x)^r x^m \cos(p \ln x)$. Or set $x = e^t$ and reduce the equation to the preceding form.

Thus if $x = e^t$, we have

$$y' = \frac{dy}{dt} \frac{dt}{dx} = \frac{1}{x} \frac{dy}{dt} \; ; \; xy' = \frac{dy}{dt}$$

$$d^2y/dt^2 = d(xy')/dt = x \, d(xy')/dx = x^2 y'' + xy'$$

$$d^3y/dt^3 = d(x^2y'' + xy')/dt = x \, d(x^2y'' + xy')/dx = x^3 y''' + 3x^2 y'' + xy'$$

589. $x^2 y'' - 4xy' + 6y = 0$.   **590.** $x^2 y'' - xy' - 3y = 0$.
591. $x^3 y''' + xy' - y = 0$.   **592.** $x^2 y''' = 2y'$.
593. $x^2 y'' - xy' + y = 8x^3$.   **594.** $x^2 y'' + xy' + 4y = 10x$.
595. $x^3 y'' - 2xy = 6 \ln x$.   **596.** $x^2 y'' - 3xy' + 5y = 3x^2$.
597. $x^2 y'' - 6y = 5x^3 + 8x^2$.   **598.** $x^2 y'' - 2y = \sin \ln x$.
599. $(x - 2)^2 y'' - 3(x - 2) y' + 4y = x$.
600. $(2x + 3)^3 y''' + 3(2x + 3) y' - 6y = 0$.

Section 12

LINEAR EQUATIONS WITH VARIABLE COEFFICIENTS

Problems 601-655 are to be solved by the use of methods described in any book on the general theory of linear differential equations. Each problem has either a hint or a reference to the literature.

When a particular solution y_1 is known for a linear equation of order n in reduced form (also called homogeneous form, or having 0 in the right member) the order of the equation can be reduced and the equation of lower order is again a linear equation. The method is to set $y = zy_1$ and then reduce the order by making the substitution $u = z'$.

In case the given equation has second order

$$a_o(x)\, y'' + a_1(x)\, y' + a_2(x)\, y = 0,$$

a convenient method for finding a general solution when one solution y_1 is known is to use the formula of Liouville-Ostrogradskii:

$$\begin{vmatrix} y_1 & y_2 \\ y_1' & y_2' \end{vmatrix} = Ce^{-\int p(x)\,dx}, \quad p(x) = \frac{a_1(x)}{a_o(x)},$$

where y_1 and y_2 are any two solutions of the given equation.

Example. We start with the known solution $y_1 = x$ of the

equation

$$(x^2 + 1)\, y'' - 2xy' + 2y = 0. \tag{1}$$

The Liouville-Ostrogradskii formula gives

$$\begin{vmatrix} y_1 & y_2 \\ y_1' & y_2' \end{vmatrix} = Ce^{-\int\left(\frac{-2x}{x^2 + 1}\right)\, dx}; \quad y_1 y_2' - y_1' y_2 = C(x^2 + 1).$$

Since the function y_1 is known, this gives a linear first

order equation for y_2. This can be solved in several ways;

for instance, if we divide the equation by y_1^2, the left mem-

ber becomes the derivative of the quotient y_2/y_1:

$$\left(\frac{y_2}{y_1}\right) = \frac{y_1 y_2' - y_1' y}{y_1^2} = \frac{C(x^2 + 1)}{y_1^2}.$$

Since $y_1 = x$, we obtain

$$\frac{y_2}{y_1} = \int C \cdot \frac{x^2 + 1}{x^2}\, dx + C_2 = C\left(x - \frac{1}{x}\right) + C_2;$$

$$y = C(x^2 - 1) + C_2 x.$$

Thus we have the general solution of equation (1).

There is no general method for finding even a particular

solution of a linear second order differential equation, but

in some cases we can find the solution of a specified form by

the method of undetermined coefficients.

Example. Let us try to find a solution of the equation

$$(1 - 2x^2) y'' + 2y' + 4y = 0 , \qquad (2)$$

which is a rational polynomial, if there is one.

The first step is to find what degree the polynomial must have. If we put in the term x^n of highest degree in equation (2) and compute the terms of highest degree throughout, we find that only the term involving the second derivative and the terms involving y will contain the term of highest degree:

$$- 2x^2 \cdot n(n-1) x^{n-2} + \ldots + 4x^n + \ldots = 0.$$

Since the coefficient of x^n must be 0, we see that the relation $- 2n(n - 1) + 4 = 0$; $n^2 - n - 2 = 0$ must hold. There are two solutions, $n = 2$, $n = -1$, the latter of which is not useful since a polynomial cannot have negative degree. Thus the polynomial has second degree and takes the form $y = x^2 + ax + b$. If we insert this in equation (2), we obtain the relation $(4a + 4) x + 2 + 2a + 4b = 0$. Therefore, $4a + 4 = 0$, $2 + 2a + 4b = 0$. This gives $a = -1$, $b = 0$. Thus the polynomial $y = x^2 - x$ is a particular solution.

In problems 601-622 determine whether the given functions

are linearly independent. In each case the functions of the

set are to be taken in the region in which all are defined.

601. $x+2$, $x-2$. **602.** $6x+9$, $8x+12$.
603. $\sin x$, $\cos x$. **604.** 1, x, x^2.
605. $4-x$, $2x+3$, $6x+8$.
606. x^2+2x, $3x^2-1$, $x+4$.
607. x^2-x+3, $2x^2+x$, $2x-4$.
608. e^x, e^{2x}, e^{3x}. **609.** x, e^x, xe^x.
610. 1, $\sin^2 x$, $\cos 2x$. **611.** $\operatorname{sh} x$, $\operatorname{ch} x$, $2+e^x$.
612. $\ln(x^2)$, $\ln 3x$, 7. **613.** x, 0, e^x.
614. $\operatorname{sh} x$, $\operatorname{ch} x$, $2e^x-1$, $3e^x+5$.
615. 2^x, 3^x, 6^x. **616.** $\sin x$, $\cos x$, $\sin 2x$.
617. $\sin x$, $\sin(x+2)$, $\cos(x-5)$.
618. $\sqrt{x}$, $\sqrt{x+1}$, $\sqrt{x+2}$.
619. $\operatorname{arctg} x$, $\operatorname{arcctg} x$, 1. **620.** x^2, $x|x|$.
621. x, $|x|$, $2x+\sqrt{4x^2}$. **622.** x, x^3, $|x^3|$.

623.[*] Let the functions $y_1(x)$ and $y_2(x)$ be linearly

independent on an interval (a,b). If these functions are dif-

ferentiable and if the determinant $y_1 y_2' - y_2 y_1'$ has the

value 0, show that there is a point x_o on the given interval

for which the relations $y_1(x_o) = y_2(x_o) = y_1'(x_o) = y_2'(x_o) = 0$ hold.

In each of the problems 624-630 find a linear homogeneous

differential equation which has the given particular solutions

and as low an order as possible.

624. 1, $\cos x$. **625.** x, e^x.
626. $3x$, $x-2$, e^x+1.
627. x^2-3x, $2x^2+9$, $2x+3$.
628. e^x, $\operatorname{sh} x$, $\operatorname{ch} x$. **629.** x, x^2, e^x.
630. x, x^3, $|x^3|$.

In problems 631-651 find the general solution of the given equation by starting with a particular solution. If no particular solution is given try to find a particular solution of the form $y_1 = e^{ax}$ or a rational polynomial $y = x^n + ax^{n-1} + bx^{n-2} + \cdots$

631. $(2x+1)y'' + 4xy' - 4y = 0.$

632. $x^2(x+1)y'' - 2y = 0; \; y_1 = 1 + \dfrac{1}{x}.$

633. $xy'' - (2x+1)y' + (x+1)y = 0.$

634. $xy'' + 2y' - xy = 0; \; y_1 = \dfrac{e^x}{x}.$

635. $y'' - 2(1 + \operatorname{tg}^2 x)y = 0; \; y_1 = \operatorname{tg} x.$

636. $x(x-1)y'' - xy' + y = 0.$

637. $(e^x+1)y'' - 2y' - e^x y = 0; \; y_1 = e^x - 1.$

638. $x^2 y'' \ln x - xy' + y = 0.$

639. $y'' - y' \operatorname{tg} x + 2y = 0; \; y_1 = \sin x.$

640. $(x^2+1)y'' + 5xy' + 4y = 0; \; y_1 = \dfrac{x}{(x^2+1)^{\frac{3}{2}}}.$

641. $xy'' - (x+1)y' - 2(x-1)y = 0.$

642. $y'' + 4xy' + (4x^2+2)y = 0; \; y_1 = e^{ax^2}.$

643. $xy'' - (2x+1)y' + 2y = 0.$

644. $x(2x+1)y'' + 2(x+1)y' - 2y = 0.$

645. $x(x+4)y'' - (2x+4)y' + 2y = 0.$

646. $x(x^2+6)y'' - 4(x^2+3)y' + 6xy = 0.$

647. $(x^2+1)y'' - 2y = 0.$

648. $2x(x+2)y'' + (2-x)y' + y = 0.$

649. $xy''' - y'' - xy' + y = 0; \; y_1 = x, \; y_2 = e^x.$

650. $x^2(2x-1)y''' + (4x-3)xy'' - 2xy' + 2y = 0;$
$$y_1 = x, \; y_2 = \frac{1}{x}.$$

651. $(x^2-2x+3)y''' - (x^2+1)y'' + 2xy' - 2y = 0;$
$$y_1 = x, \; y_2 = e^x.$$

Find a general solution of the linear non-homogeneous equations given, knowing that a particular solution of the corresponding homogeneous (reduced) equation is a polynomial.

652. $(x+1)xy'' + (x+2)y' - y = x + \dfrac{1}{x}.$

653. $(2x+1)y'' + (2x-1)y' - 2y = x^2 + x.$

Knowing two particular solutions of the linear non-homogeneous second order given, find the general solution.

654. $(x^2 - 1) y'' + 4xy' + 2y = 6x;$
$$y_1 = x, \quad y_2 = \frac{x^2 + x + 1}{x + 1}.$$

655. $(3x^3 + x) y'' + 2y' - 6xy = 4 - 12x^2;$
$$y_1 = 2x, \quad y_2 = (x + 1)^2.$$

In problems 656-660 make a substitution $y = a(x)z$ to obtain a differential equation with the term involving the first derivative absent.

656. $x^2 y'' - 2xy' + (x^2 + 2) y = 0.$
657. $x^2 y'' - 4xy' + (6 - x^2) y = 0.$
658. $(1 + x^2) y'' + 4xy' + 2y = 0.$
659. $x^2 y'' + 2x^2 y' + (x^2 - 2) y = 0.$
660. $xy'' + y' + xy = 0.$

In problems 661-665 change the independent variable by the formula $t = \phi(x)$ so that the term involving the first derivative is absent. Note that the function $\phi(x)$ is not uniquely defined by the requirements of the problem because if $\phi(x)$ solves the problem, so does $a\phi(x) + b$ for arbitrary constant a,b.

661. $xy'' - y' - 4x^3 y = 0.$
662. $(1 + x^2) y'' + xy' + y = 0.$
663. $x^2 (1 - x^2) y'' + 2 (x - x^3) y' - 2y = 0.$
664. $y'' - y' + e^{2x} y = 0.$
665. $2xy'' + y' + xy = 0.$

666. Find the distance between two adjacent zeros of a solution ($\not\equiv 0$) of the equation $y'' + my = 0$, where m is a positive constant. How many zeros can be contained on the interval $a \leq x \leq b$?

In problems 667-670 use the Sturm-Liouville theory to find the largest and smallest possible numbers of zeros of a solution of the corresponding equation, providing the solution is not identically 0, on the given interval.

667. $y'' + 2xy = 0, \ 20 \leqslant x \leqslant 45.$
668. $xy'' + y = 0, \ \ 25 \leqslant x \leqslant 100.$
669. $y'' - 2xy' + (x+1)^2 y = 0, \ 4 \leqslant x \leqslant 19.$
670. $y'' - 2e^x y' + e^{2x} y = 0, \ \ \ \ 2 \leqslant x \leqslant 6.$

671.* Solve the corresponding problem for the equation $y'' + xy = 0$ on the segment $-25 \leq x \leq 25$.

672. Let $x_1, x_2, \ldots$ be the distinct zeros, arranged in ascending order, of a solution of the equation $y'' + q(x)y = 0$, where $q(x) > 0$. Suppose the function $q(x)$ is continuous and increasing for $A < x < \infty$. Show that the relation $x_{n+1} - x_n < x_n - x_{n-1}$ holds; that is that the distance between successive zeros decreases.

673. In the preceding problem let c be the finite limit or ∞, of the function $q(x)$ as $x \to \infty$. Show that the relation

$$\lim_{n \to \infty} (x_{n+1} - x_n) = \frac{\pi}{\sqrt{c}}$$

holds.

674.[*] Let the functions $y(x)$ and $z(x)$ satisfy the equations $y'' + q(x) y = 0$ and $z'' + Q(x) z = 0$, let $y(x)$ be positive on the segment (x_1, x_2) and let $z(x)$ be positive on the segment (x_1, x_2^*), and 0 at each end point. Suppose $Q(x) > q(x) > 0$. Show that if the relation $z'(x_1) \leq y'(x_1)$ holds, then for all x on $x_1 < x \leq x_2^*$, the relation $z(x) < y(x)$ holds.

675.[*] In connection with problem 672, set

$$b_n = \max_{x_n \leq x \leq x_{n+1}} y(x) .$$

Show that $b_1 > b_2 > b_3 > \cdots$

676.[*] In problem 673, suppose the limit c is finite. Show that $b_n \to B > 0$, for $n \to \infty$, where b_n is defined in problem 675.

677. By a change $t = \phi(x)$ of the independent variable, rewrite the equation $d^2y/dx^2 \pm y/(\psi(x))^4 = 0$ in the form $d^2y/dt^2 + b(t)\,dy/dt \pm y = 0$, and then remove the term involving the first derivative by making the substitution $y = a(t)\,u$.

Note: This transformation is due to Liouville. This transformation converts the equation $y'' + q(x)\,y = 0$ into an equation of the same form, but with coefficients that are nearly constant, that is that change very little on the interval (t_o, ∞). In that way it may be possible to obtain information about the behavior of the solution in the limit $x \to \infty$.

678.* Suppose the relation $|f(t)| \leq c/t^{1+d}$, for some positive $d > 0$. Show that there are two solutions $u_1(t)$, $u_2(t)$ of the equation $u'' + (1 + f(t))\,u = 0$ with the properties $u_1(t) = \cos t + 0\,(t^{-d})$, $u_2(t) = \sin t + 0\,(t^{-d})$, $t \to \infty$.

Hint. Transpose the term $f(t)\,u$ to the right member, denote this term by $F(t)$ and use the method of variation of constants. The integrals involved in the solution by this method are to have upper limit $+\infty$. Then use the method of successive approximations, taking the initial approximation to be $u = \cos t$ $\left[u = \sin t.\right]$

679.[*] Under the same hypothesis as in 678, consider the equation $u'' - (1 - f(t))\, u = 0$ and obtain the relations

$$u_1(t) = e^t(1 + 0(t^{-d})), \quad u_2(t) = e^{-t}(1 + 0(t^{-d})).$$

In problems 680-688 use the method of Liouville, explained after problem 677, to find the asymptotic behavior of the solutions of the given equation $x \to \infty$. Make use of the assertions of problems 678, 679.

680. $y'' + x^2 y = 0$.   681. $y'' + e^{2x} y = 0$.

682. $xy'' - y = 0$.   683. $y'' - xy = 0$.

684. $xy'' + 2y' + y = 0$.

685. $y'' - 2(x-1) y' + x^2 y = 0$.

686*. $y'' + (x^4 + 1) y = 0$.   687*. $(x^2 + 1) y'' - y = 0$.

688*. $x^2 y'' + y \ln^2 x = 0$.

In problems 689-690 use Liouville's transformation twice to get two terms in the asymptotic behavior of the solutions of the given equations.

689. $y'' - 4x^2 y = 0$.   690. $xy'' + y = 0$.

Section 13

SERIES DEVELOPMENT OF SOLUTIONS OF EQUATIONS

A function $f(x,y)$ that is analytic in the neighborhood of the point (x_o, y_o) can be expanded in a series of powers of $(x-x_o)$ and $(y-y_o)$. Moreover, the equation $y' = f(x,y)$ has a solution that takes the initial value $y(x_o) = y_o$ and is an analytic function of x. This is shown in standard works on the existence of solutions of differential equations. A corresponding theorem holds for an equation of the form

$$y^{(n)} = f(x,y,y',\ldots y^{(n-1)})$$ with initial conditions

$$y(x_o) = y_o, \; y'(x_o) = y_o,\ldots,y^{(n-1)}(x_o) = y_o^{(n-1)}.$$

Example. To find a series solution for the equation $y'' = xy^2 - y'$ having initial values $y(0) = 2$, $y'(0) = 1$.

Suppose the series starts as follows

$$y = a_o + a_1 x + a_2 x^2 + \ldots = 2 + x + a_2 x^2 + a_3 x^3 + \ldots, \quad (1)$$

the first two terms having been obtained from the initial values. If we substitute this series in the differential equation, we obtain $2a_2 + 6a_3 x + 12a_4 x^2 + \ldots$

$$= x(2 + x + a_2 x^2 + \ldots)^2 - 1 - 2a_2 x - 3a_3 x^2 - \ldots$$

We must now expand the indicated square in the right member and compare coefficients of corresponding powers of x on both sides. This gives $2a_2 = -1$, $6a_3 = 4 - 2a_2$, $12a_4 = 4 - 3a_3$,... from which we obtain $a_2 = -1/2$, $a_3 = 5/6$, $a_4 = 1/8$, ...

Therefore, $y = 2 + x - (1/2)x^2 + (5/6)x^3 + (1/8)x^4 + \ldots$

If we have to solve an equation

$$p_0(x) \, y^{(n)} + p_1(x) \, y^{(n-1)} + \ldots + p_n(x) \, y = 0, \qquad (2)$$

and it happens that $p_0(x_0) = 0$, that is that the coefficient of the highest derivative is zero at the point x_0, there may be no solution in series, but there may be a solution of the form

$$a_0(x - x_0)^r + a_1(x - x_0)^{r+1} + a_2(x - x_0)^{r+2} + \ldots, (3)$$

where the number r is not necessarily a positive integer. The value of r, if there is a suitable one, is found by substituting this series into equation (2) and trying to compare the lowest powers of $(x - x_0)$. Having determined r, one then proceeds to determine the coefficients a_i.

In each of the problems 691-697 find a solution in series which satisfies the given conditions. Compute the first few terms of the series up to the term involving x^4.

691. $y' = y^2 - x$; $y(0) = 1$. **692.** $y' = x + \dfrac{1}{y}$; $y(0) = 1$.

693. $y' = y + xe^y$; $y(0) = 0$.

694. $y' = 2x + \cos y$; $y(0) = 0$.

695. $y' = x^2 + y^3$; $y(1) = 1$.

696. $y'' = xy' - y^2$; $y(0) = 1$, $y'(0) = 2$.

697. $y'' = y'^2 + xy$; $y(0) = 4$, $y'(0) = -2$.

698.* Use the relation $- x < y' < 1 + y^2$, valid for $-1 < x < 1$, to give a lower estimate for the radius of convergence of a power series which represents the solution of the equation $y' = y^2 - x$ with initial value $y(0) = 1$.

699.* Calculate the accuracy with which a solution of the equation $y' = e^y - x^2 y$, with initial condition $y(0) = 0$, is obtained by the use of a series solution going as far as the term involving x^4, if values of x are restricted to have absolute value less than 0.2.

In problems 700–709 find the linearly independent solutions of each of the given equations in the form of series. When possible, sum the series and express the solutions in terms of elementary functions.

700. $y'' - x^2 y = 0$. **701.** $y'' - xy' - 2y = 0$.

702. $(1 - x^2) y'' - 4xy' - 2y = 0$.

703. $(x^2 + 1) y'' + 5xy' + 3y = 0$.

704. $(1 - x) y'' - 2y' + y = 0$.

705. $(x^2 - x + 1) y'' + (4x - 2) y' + 2y = 0$.

706. $y'' - xy' + xy = 0$. **707.** $y'' + y \sin x = 0$.

708. $xy'' + y \ln(1 - x) = 0$.

709. $y''' - xy'' + (x - 2) y' + y = 0$.

In problems 710-716 find those solutions of the given equations which can be expressed as power series or a generalized power series, Equation (3) above.

710. $xy'' + 2y' + xy = 0.$
711. $2x^2y'' + (3x - 2x^2)y' - (x + 1)y = 0.$
712. $9x^2y'' - (x^2 - 2)y = 0.$
713. $x^2y'' - x^2y' + (x - 2)y = 0.$
714. $x^2y'' + 2xy' - (x^2 + 2x + 2)y = 0.$
715. $xy'' - xy' - y = 0.$ **716.** $xy'' + y' - xy = 0.$

717. For the solution of problem 716 which is independent of the series solutions found above, find the behavior of the solution, $x \to 0$, to the term of order less than x^5.

In problems 718-720 determine whether solutions exist in the form of power series or generalized power series, see Equation (3) above.

718. $x^2y'' + xy' - (x + 2)y = 0.$
719. $x^2y'' + xy' + (1 - x)y = 0.$
720. $x^2y' + (x - 1)y = -1.$

In problems 721-722 find periodic solutions of the equations in the form of trigonometric series

$$a_0 + a_1 \cos x + b_1 \sin x + a_2 \cos 2x + b_2 \sin 2x \ldots$$

<u>Hint</u>. In problem 722 express the right member as a Fourier series of the form $\Sigma\, 2^{-n} \sin nx$.

721. $y'' + y' + y = |\sin x|.$

722. $y''' - y' - y = \dfrac{2 \sin x}{5 - 4 \cos x}.$

In problems 723-725 develop 2-3 terms of the solution as a series of powers of the parameter μ . Note that the fact that such a series in powers of μ exists follows from the assertion that the solution is an analytic function of μ , as shown in standard works on differential equations. See Sec. 18.

723. $y' = 4\mu(x + 1) - y^2;$ $\quad y(0) = 1.$

724. $y' = \dfrac{2}{y} - 5\mu x;$ $\quad\quad\ y(1) = 2.$

725. $xy' = \mu x^2 + \ln y;$ $\quad\ \ y(1) = 1.$

Section 14

LINEAR SYSTEMS WITH CONSTANT COEFFICIENTS

A linear system with constant coefficients can be solved
either by eliminating the unknowns (this process requires
successive differentiations, and requires that the constants
of the solutions so obtained be evaluated by substituting in
the original equations) or can be solved by studying the characteristic equation in determinantal form. A non-homogeneous
system of equations can be solved by obtaining particular
solutions by the method of variation of constants. If the
right members have special forms (polynomials in x,   exponen-
tials, sines, cosines, or sums of terms of this form) particular
solutions can always be found by the method of undetermined coefficients as in the case of single equations of corresponding
types.

In problems 726-752 solve the given system of equations.
The symbol $\dot{x}$ is used for dx/dt, $\dot{y}$ for dy/dt, $\dot{z}$ for dz/dt.
The roots of the characteristic equation are indicated in some
problems.

726. $\begin{cases} \dot{x} = 2x + y, \\ \dot{y} = 3x + 4y. \end{cases}$

727. $\begin{cases} \dot{x} = x - y, \\ \dot{y} = y - 4x. \end{cases}$

728. $\begin{cases} \dot{x} + x - 8y = 0, \\ \dot{y} - x - y = 0. \end{cases}$

729. $\begin{cases} \dot{x} = x + y, \\ \dot{y} = 3y - 2x. \end{cases}$

730. $\begin{cases} \dot{x} = x - 3y, \\ \dot{y} = 3x + y. \end{cases}$

731. $\begin{cases} \dot{x} + x + 5y = 0. \\ \dot{y} - x - y = 0. \end{cases}$

732. $\begin{cases} \dot{x} = 2x + y, \\ \dot{y} = 4y - x. \end{cases}$

733. $\begin{cases} \dot{x} = 3x - y, \\ \dot{y} = 4x - y. \end{cases}$

734. $\begin{cases} \dot{x} = 2y - 3x, \\ \dot{y} = y - 2x. \end{cases}$

735. $\begin{cases} \dot{x} - 5x - 3y = 0, \\ \dot{y} + 3x + y = 0. \end{cases}$

736. $\begin{cases} \dot{x} = x + z - y, \\ \dot{y} = x + y - z, \\ \dot{z} = 2x - y \end{cases}$

$(\lambda_1 = 1, \ \lambda_2 = 2, \ \lambda_3 = -1).$

737. $\begin{cases} \dot{x} = x - 2y - z, \\ \dot{y} = y - x + z, \\ \dot{z} = x - z \end{cases}$

$(\lambda_1 = 0, \ \lambda_2 = 2, \ \lambda_3 = -1).$

738. $\begin{cases} \dot{x} = 2x - y + z, \\ \dot{y} = x + 2y - z, \\ \dot{z} = x - y + 2z \end{cases}$

$(\lambda_1 = 1, \ \lambda_2 = 2, \ \lambda_3 = 3).$

739. $\begin{cases} \dot{x} = 3x - y + z, \\ \dot{y} = x + y + z, \\ \dot{z} = 4x - y + 4z \end{cases}$

$(\lambda_1 = 1, \ \lambda_2 = 2, \ \lambda_3 = 5).$

740. $\begin{cases} \dot{x} = 4y - 2z - 3x, \\ \dot{y} = z + x, \\ \dot{z} = 6x - 6y + 5z \end{cases}$

$(\lambda_1 = 1, \lambda_2 = 2, \lambda_3 = -1).$

741. $\begin{cases} \dot{x} = x - y - z, \\ \dot{y} = x + y, \\ \dot{z} = 3x + z \end{cases}$

$(\lambda_1 = 1, \ \lambda_{2.3} = 1 \pm 2i).$

742. $\begin{cases} \dot{x} = 2x + y, \\ \dot{y} = x + 3y - z, \\ \dot{z} = 2y + 3z - x \end{cases}$

$(\lambda_1 = 2, \ \lambda_{2.3} = 3 \pm i).$

743. $\begin{cases} \dot{x} = 2x + 2z - y, \\ \dot{y} = x + 2z, \\ \dot{z} = y - 2x - z \end{cases}$

$(\lambda_1 = 1, \ \lambda_{2.3} = \pm i).$

744. $\begin{cases} \dot{x} = 4x - y - z, \\ \dot{y} = x + 2y - z, \\ \dot{z} = x - y + 2z \end{cases}$

$(\lambda_1 = 2, \ \lambda_2 = \lambda_3 = 3).$

745. $\begin{cases} \dot{x} = 2x - y - z, \\ \dot{y} = 3x - 2y - 3z, \\ \dot{z} = 2z - x + y \end{cases}$

$(\lambda_1 = 0, \ \lambda_2 = \lambda_3 = 1).$

746. $\begin{cases} \dot{x} = y - 2x - 2z, \\ \dot{y} = x - 2y + 2z, \\ \dot{z} = 3x - 3y + 5z \end{cases}$
$(\lambda_1 = 3, \ \lambda_2 = \lambda_3 = -1).$

747. $\begin{cases} \dot{x} = 3x - 2y - z, \\ \dot{y} = 3x - 4y - 3z, \\ \dot{z} = 2x - 4y \end{cases}$
$(\lambda_1 = \lambda_2 = 2, \ \lambda_3 = -5).$

748. $\begin{cases} \dot{x} = x - y + z, \\ \dot{y} = x + y - z, \\ \dot{z} = 2z - y \end{cases}$
$(\lambda_1 = \lambda_2 = 1, \ \lambda_3 = 2).$

749. $\begin{cases} \dot{x} = y - 2z - x, \\ \dot{y} = 4x + y, \\ \dot{z} = 2x + y - z \end{cases}$
$(\lambda_1 = 1, \ \lambda_2 = \lambda_3 = -1).$

750. $\begin{cases} \dot{x} = 2x + y, \\ \dot{y} = 2y + 4z, \\ \dot{z} = x - z \end{cases}$
$(\lambda_1 = \lambda_2 = 0, \ \lambda_3 = 3).$

751. $\begin{cases} \dot{x} = 2x - y - z, \\ \dot{y} = 2x - y - 2z, \\ \dot{z} = 2z - x + y \end{cases}$
$(\lambda_1 = \lambda_2 = \lambda_3 = 1).$

752. $\begin{cases} \dot{x} = 4x - y, \\ \dot{y} = 3x + y - z, \\ \dot{z} = x + z \end{cases}$
$(\lambda_1 = \lambda_2 = \lambda_3 = 2).$

In problems 753-765 solve the systems without necessarily

reducing them to normal forms.

753. $\begin{cases} \ddot{x} = 2x - 3y, \\ \ddot{y} = x - 2y. \end{cases}$

754. $\begin{cases} \ddot{x} = 3x + 4y, \\ \ddot{y} = -x - y. \end{cases}$

755. $\begin{cases} \ddot{x} = 2y, \\ \ddot{y} = -2x. \end{cases}$

756. $\begin{cases} \ddot{x} = 3x - y - z, \\ \ddot{y} = -x + 3y - z, \\ \ddot{z} = -x - y + 3z. \end{cases}$

757. $\begin{cases} 2\dot{x} - 5\dot{y} = 4y - x, \\ 3\dot{x} - 4\dot{y} = 2x - y. \end{cases}$

758. $\begin{cases} \ddot{x} + \dot{x} + \dot{y} - 2y = 0, \\ \dot{x} - \dot{y} + x = 0. \end{cases}$

759. $\begin{cases} \ddot{x} - 2\ddot{y} + \dot{y} + x - 3y = 0, \\ 4\ddot{y} - 2\ddot{x} - \dot{x} - 2x + 5y = 0. \end{cases}$

760. $\begin{cases} \ddot{x} - x + 2\ddot{y} - 2y = 0, \\ \dot{x} - x + \dot{y} + y = 0. \end{cases}$

761. $\begin{cases} \ddot{x} - 2\dot{y} + 2x = 0, \\ 3\dot{x} + \dot{y} - 8y = 0. \end{cases}$

762. $\begin{cases} \ddot{x} + 3\ddot{y} - x = 0, \\ \dot{x} + 3\dot{y} - 2y = 0. \end{cases}$

763. $\begin{cases} \ddot{x} + 5\dot{x} + 2\dot{y} + y = 0, \\ 3\ddot{x} + 5x + \dot{y} + 3y = 0. \end{cases}$

764. $\begin{cases} \ddot{x} + 4\dot{x} - 2x - 2\dot{y} - y = 0, \\ \ddot{x} - 4\dot{x} - \ddot{y} + 2\dot{y} + 2y = 0. \end{cases}$

765. $\begin{cases} 2\ddot{x} + 2\dot{x} + x + 3\ddot{y} + \dot{y} + y = 0, \\ \ddot{x} + 4\dot{x} - x + 3\ddot{y} + 2\dot{y} - y = 0. \end{cases}$

In problems 766-785 solve the non-linear non-homogeneous systems.

766. $\begin{cases} \dot{x} = y + 2e^t, \\ \dot{y} = x + t^2. \end{cases}$

767. $\begin{cases} \dot{x} = y - 5\cos t, \\ \dot{y} = 2x + y. \end{cases}$

768. $\begin{cases} \dot{x} = 3x + 2y + 4e^{5t}, \\ \dot{y} = x + 2y. \end{cases}$

769. $\begin{cases} \dot{x} = 3x - 4y + e^{-2t}, \\ \dot{y} = x - 2y - 3e^{-2t}. \end{cases}$

770. $\begin{cases} \dot{x} = 4x + y - e^{2t}, \\ \dot{y} = y - 2x. \end{cases}$

771. $\begin{cases} \dot{x} = 2y - x + 1, \\ \dot{y} = 3y - 2x. \end{cases}$

772. $\begin{cases} \dot{x} = 5x - 3y + 2e^{3t}, \\ \dot{y} = x + y + 5e^{-t}. \end{cases}$

773. $\begin{cases} \dot{x} = x + y + 1 + e^t, \\ \dot{y} = 3x - y. \end{cases}$

774. $\begin{cases} \dot{x} = x + 2y, \\ \dot{y} = x - 5\sin t. \end{cases}$

775. $\begin{cases} \dot{x} = 2x - 4y, \\ \dot{y} = x - 3y + 3e^t. \end{cases}$

776. $\begin{cases} \dot{x} = 2x - y, \\ \dot{y} = y - 2x + 18t. \end{cases}$

777. $\begin{cases} \dot{x} = x + 2y + 16te^t, \\ \dot{y} = 2x - 2y. \end{cases}$

778. $\begin{cases} \dot{x} = 2x + 4y - 8, \\ \dot{y} = 3x + 6y. \end{cases}$

779. $\begin{cases} \dot{x} = 2x - 3y, \\ \dot{y} = x - 2y + 2\sin t. \end{cases}$

780. $\begin{cases} \dot{x} = 2x + 3y + 5t, \\ \dot{y} = 3x + 2y + 8e^t. \end{cases}$

781. $\begin{cases} \dot{x} = 2x - y, \\ \dot{y} = x + 2e^t. \end{cases}$

782. $\begin{cases} \dot{x} = 4x - 3y + \sin t, \\ \dot{y} = 2x - y - 2\cos t. \end{cases}$

783. $\begin{cases} \dot{x} = 2x + y + 2e^t, \\ \dot{y} = x + 2y - 3e^{1t}. \end{cases}$

784. $\begin{cases} \dot{x} = x - y + 8t, \\ \dot{y} = 5x - y. \end{cases}$

785. $\begin{cases} \dot{x} = 2x - y, \\ \dot{y} = 2y - x - 5e^t\sin t. \end{cases}$

In problems 786-790 solve the given systems by the method of variation of constants.

786. $\begin{cases} \dot{x} = y + \mathrm{tg}^2 t - 1, \\ \dot{y} = -x + \mathrm{tg}\, t. \end{cases}$ **787.** $\begin{cases} \dot{x} = 2y - x, \\ \dot{y} = 4y - 3x + \dfrac{e^{3t}}{e^{2t} + 1}. \end{cases}$

788. $\begin{cases} \dot{x} = -4x - 2y + \dfrac{2}{e^t - 1}, \\ \dot{y} = 6x + 3y - \dfrac{3}{e^t - 1}. \end{cases}$

789. $\begin{cases} \dot{x} = x - y + \dfrac{1}{\cos t}, \\ \dot{y} = 2x - y. \end{cases}$ **790.** $\begin{cases} \dot{x} = 3x - 2y, \\ \dot{y} = 2x - y + 15e^t \sqrt{t}. \end{cases}$

Section 15

LYAPUNOV STABILITY

Foundations of Lyapunov's stability theory are to be found in several books. See for example, the Introduction of: Krasovskii, The Theory of Motion, Stanford University Press, 1963; Coddington and Levinson, Differential Equations, McGraw-Hill, 1952; Lefschetz and LaSalle, Stability Theory of Differential Equations, Prentice-Hall, 1962.

791. Use the definition of Lyapunov's stability to decide whether the solution of the equation $dx/dt = t - x$, with initial value $x(0) = 1$, is stable or unstable.

792. Answer the same question for the solution of the system

$$dx/dt = 4y, \quad dy/dt = -x$$

with initial conditions $x(0) = 0$, $y(0) = 0$.

In problems 793-796 use Lyapunov's theorem on first order stability to determine whether the trivial solution $x(t) = 0$, $y(t) = 0$ is a stable solution of the given system.

793. $\begin{cases} \dot{x} = 2xy - x + y, \\ \dot{y} = 5x^4 + y^3 + 2x - 3y. \end{cases}$ **794** $\begin{cases} \dot{x} = x^2 + y^2 - 2x, \\ \dot{y} = 3x^2 - x + 3y. \end{cases}$

795. $\begin{cases} \dot{x} = e^{x+2y} - \cos 3x, \\ \dot{y} = \sqrt{4 + 8x} - 2e^y. \end{cases}$ **796.** $\begin{cases} \dot{x} = \ln(4y + e^{-3x}), \\ \dot{y} = 2y - 1 + \sqrt[3]{1 - 6x}. \end{cases}$

In problems 797-800 find the equilibrium point and determine whether it is a stable or unstable solution.

797. $\begin{cases} \dot{x} = y - x^2 - x, \\ \dot{y} = 3x - x^2 - y. \end{cases}$ **798.** $\begin{cases} \dot{x} = (x - 1)(y - 1), \\ \dot{y} = xy - 2. \end{cases}$

799. $\begin{cases} \dot{x} = 5 - x^2 - y^2, \\ \dot{y} = 1 + y^2 - x. \end{cases}$ **800.** $\begin{cases} \dot{x} = y, \\ \dot{y} = \sin(x + y). \end{cases}$

801. Determine whether the solution $x = t$, $y = -t^2$ is a stable solution of the system $\begin{cases} \dot{x} = \ln(1 + 2t - 2x) + 3y + 3t^2 + 1, \\ \dot{y} = x^2 - 2tx - 2x - y. \end{cases}$

802. A certain system of equations has for solutions the family

$$x = \frac{C_1 - C_2 t}{1 + t^2}, \qquad y = (C_1 t^3 + C_2)e^{-t}.$$

Determine whether the null-solution $x(t) = 0$, $y(t) = 0$ is a stable solution of the system.

803. Suppose the functions $P(x,y)$, $Q(x,y)$ are continuous and have continuous first derivatives, and furthermore reduce to zero at the origin. Suppose further that the trajectories of the system $dx/dt = P(x,y)$, $dy/dt = Q(x,y)$ have the form

given in the figure. What can be said about the behavior of every

solution for $t \to +\infty$? Is the origin an asymptotically stable

solution of the system?

804. Suppose $a(t)$ is a continuous

function of t. Show that a necessary

and sufficient condition that the null

solution of the equation

$$dx/dt = a(t) \, x$$

be stable is that the relation

$$\overline{\lim_{t \to +\infty}} \int_0^t a(s)ds < +\infty$$

hold.

805.[*] Show that if any particular solution of a linear

system of differential equations is stable, then every solution

of the same system is stable.

In problems 806-810, use a Lyapunov function to settle

the stability of the null solution of the given system. See

the Krasovskii reference cited at the beginning of this section.

806. $\begin{cases} \dot{x} = x^3 - y, \\ \dot{y} = x + y^3. \end{cases}$ 807. $\begin{cases} \dot{x} = y - x + xy, \\ \dot{y} = x - y - x^2 - y^3. \end{cases}$

808. $\begin{cases} \dot{x} = 2y^3 - x^5, \\ \dot{y} = -x - y^3 + y^5. \end{cases}$ 809. $\begin{cases} \dot{x} = y - 3x - x^3, \\ \dot{y} = 6x - 2y. \end{cases}$

810[*]. $\begin{cases} \dot{x} = -f_1(x) - f_2(y), \\ \dot{y} = f_3(x) - f_4(y), \end{cases}$

where $\operatorname{sgn} \, f_i(z) = \operatorname{sgn} z$, $i = 1,2,3,4$.

Section 16

SINGULAR POINTS

If the functions $P(x,y)$, $Q(x,y)$ have continuous derivatives with respect to both arguments, the points (x,y) that verify both the equations $P(x,y) = 0$, $Q(x,y) = 0$ are called singular points of the equation

$$dy/dx = P(x,y)/Q(x,y) \qquad (1)$$

or of the system

$$dx/dt = P(x,y), \quad dy/dt = Q(x,y) \; . \qquad (2)$$

Consider the system

$$dx/dt = ax + by \; , \quad dy/dt = cx + dy, \qquad (3)$$

or the single equation

$$dy/dx = (cx + dy)/(ax + by) \; , \qquad (4)$$

where a,b,c,d are real constants.

First suppose that the determinant

$$\det \begin{bmatrix} a & b \\ c & d \end{bmatrix} \qquad (5)$$

does not have the value zero.

Then the singular points can be characterized by examining the characteristic roots, that is the solutions of the determinantal equation

$$\det \begin{bmatrix} a - \lambda \ , \ c \\ \\ b \ , \quad d - \lambda \end{bmatrix} = 0 \ .$$

i. If the characteristic roots are real, distinct, and of the same sign, the singular point is a node (fig. 2i).

ii. If the characteristic roots are real and distinct but of opposite sign, the singular point is a saddle point (fig. 2ii).

iii. If the characteristic roots are neither real nor pure imaginary, the singular point is a focus (fig. 2iii).

iv. If the characteristic roots are pure imaginary, the singular point is a center (fig 2iv).

v. If the characteristic roots are equal, but nonzero, the singular point can be a degenerate node or a singular node. The latter case occurs if the equations have the form $dx/dt = ax$, $dy/dt = ay$ (or $dy/dx = y/x$); see fig. 2vi. The former case occurs otherwise. See fig. 2v.

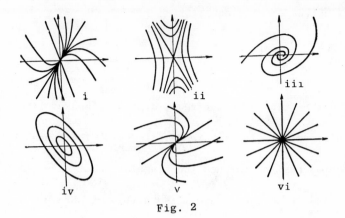

Fig. 2

The case when the determinant   ad - bc   is zero does not really require discussion.   In this case   cx + dy   is proportional to   ax + by,   and the equation has the form   dy/dx = k, or   dx/dy = k',   and the trajectories are parallel lines.

The family of trajectories in the plane is conveniently drawn by marking first those trajectories that are straight lines and pass through the node, saddle, or degenerate node. For a focus, it is necessary to find the direction the trajectories take in winding around the singular point.   These ideas are illustrated in the examples below.

Example 1.   Find the nature of the singular point of the equation

$$dy/dx = (x + y)/(2x).$$ (6)

The characteristic equation is

$$\det \begin{bmatrix} 2 - \lambda\ ,\ 0 \\ 1\ \ \ ,\ 1 - \lambda \end{bmatrix} = 0; \quad (2 - \lambda)(1 - \lambda) = 0; \quad \lambda = 1,\ \lambda = 2.$$

The characteristic roots are real, distinct, and of like sign.

Thus the singular point is a node, fig. 2i. The lines that are

trajectories passing through the singular point have the form

$y = kx$, and if we substitute this in (6), we obtain

$$k = (x + kx)/(2x), \quad 2k = 1 + k, \quad k = 1.$$

This gives the line $y = x$, but there should be two lines,

since the node is not degenerate. The missing line must be the

only one that goes through $(0,0)$ and does not have an equation

of the form $y = kx$, namely the line $x = 0$. This latter is

indeed a solution of the equation $dx/dy = 2x/(x + y)$, or of

the system $dx/dt = 2x$, $dy/dt = x + y$.

The entire system of trajectories can be sketched by draw-

ing the graph of the differential equation. For example, at

every point on the line $y = -3x$, y' has the value -1, and

the line elements drawn on this line show the direction taken

by trajectories that intersect it. Similarly on the line

$y = -x$, the slope is 0. Next, note from fig. 3a that the

intergral curves that enter the sector between the line $y = -3x$

and $x = 0$ cannot leave this sector. Therefore they are

all tangent to the line x = 0, and the trajectory curves are

as in fig. 3b.

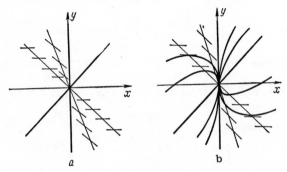

Fig. 3

Example 2. Find the character of the singular point of

the equation

$$\frac{dy}{dx} = \frac{4x - 3y}{x - 2y} \ . \tag{7}$$

The characteristic equation in this case is

$$\det \begin{bmatrix} 1 - \lambda, \ -2 \\ \\ 4 \ , \ -3 - \lambda \end{bmatrix} = 0, \ \lambda^2 + 2\lambda + 5 = 0; \lambda = -1 \pm 2 \ i.$$

The singular point is a focus. It is desirable to consider

rather than (7), the system

$$dx/dt = x - 2y, \quad dy/dt = 4x - 3y.$$

Let us draw the velocity vector (dx/dt,dy/dt) in the point

(1,0). By (8), the formula for its components is

$(x - 2y, 4x - 3y)$, that is $(1,4)$. See fig. 4a.

Thus as t increases, the direction of motion is as indicated by the arrow. Since the real part of the characteristic roots is -1 (i.e. is negative), the focus is asymptotically stable; thus the trajectories wind tighter and tighter about the singular point as t increases. The integral curves have the form of fig. 4b.

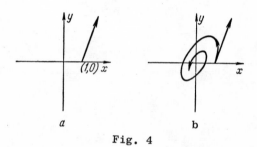

a b

Fig. 4

For equations (1) or (2), the method of studying singular points is to expand the functions $P(x,y)$, $Q(x,y)$ in a Taylor series about the singular point. System (1) then takes the form

$$\frac{dx_1}{d\tau} = ax_1 + by_1 + \phi(x_1, y_1), \quad \frac{dy_1}{dt} = cx_1 + dy_1 + \psi(x_1, y_1). \qquad (9)$$

where x_1, y_1 are the new (translated) coordinates $x - h$, $y - k$, and a,b,c,d are constants. The case we can study is that in which the relations

$$\frac{\varphi(x_1, y_1)}{r^{1+\varepsilon}} \to 0, \quad \frac{\psi(x_1, y_1)}{r^{1+\varepsilon}} \to 0$$

hold for $x \to 0$, $y \to 0$, where $r = \sqrt{x^2 + y^2}$.

This condition is clearly satisfied for $0 < \epsilon < 1$, if the

functions P,Q are twice differentiable at the point (h,k).

If all the characteristic roots of equation (5) have nonzero

real part, the singular point of system (9) will have the same

type as the singular point of the corresponding system (3) that

is obtained by neglecting the functions ϕ, ψ in (9).

Indeed the trajectories of equation (9) approach those of equa-

tion (3) as a point moves along a trajectory towards the singu-

lar point. However, to the line $y = kx$ in (3) there may well

correspond a slightly distorted line (a curve) from equation (9).

The curves of the one system also approach those of the other

when the singular point is a focus.

However, when the singular point of (3) is a center, the

singular point of (9) can be either a center or a focus (usually

the latter). If the singular point of (9) is asymptotically

stable for $t \to \infty$ or $t \to -\infty$, it will

be a focus. If a Lyapunov function can be constructed to settle

this question, the singular point will be completely described.

If the integral curves of (9) have an axis of symmetry passing

through the singular point, and if that point is a center for

(3), then it will be a center for (9). (This condition is

sufficient, but not necessary.) In particular, there is an

axis of symmetry if P(x,y), Q(x,y) are unchanged when x is

replaced by 2h - x, or if they are unchanged when y is re-

placed by 2k - y.

Find the character of the singular points in problems

811-828. Sketch the integral curves in the (x,y)-plane.

811. $y' = \dfrac{2x+y}{3x+4y}$.

812. $y' = \dfrac{x-4y}{2y-3x}$.

813. $y' = \dfrac{y-2x}{y}$.

814. $y' = \dfrac{x+4y}{2x+3y}$.

815. $y' = \dfrac{x-2y}{3x-4y}$.

816. $y' = \dfrac{2x-y}{x-y}$.

817. $y' = \dfrac{y-2x}{2y-3x}$.

818. $y' = \dfrac{4y-2x}{x+y}$.

819. $y' = \dfrac{y}{x}$.

820. $y' = \dfrac{4x-y}{3x-2y}$.

821. $\begin{cases} \dot{x} = 3x, \\ \dot{y} = 2x+y. \end{cases}$

822. $\begin{cases} \dot{x} = x+2y, \\ \dot{y} = 5y-2x. \end{cases}$

823. $\begin{cases} \dot{x} = x+3y, \\ \dot{y} = -6x-5y. \end{cases}$

824. $\begin{cases} \dot{x} = x, \\ \dot{y} = 2x-y. \end{cases}$

825. $\begin{cases} \dot{x} = -2x-5y, \\ \dot{y} = 2x+2y. \end{cases}$

826. $\begin{cases} \dot{x} = 3x+y, \\ \dot{y} = y-x. \end{cases}$

827. $\begin{cases} \dot{x} = 3x-2y, \\ \dot{y} = 4y-6x. \end{cases}$

828. $\begin{cases} \dot{x} = y-2x, \\ \dot{y} = 2y-4x. \end{cases}$

Find both the singular points and their character in problems 829-832.

829. $y' = \dfrac{2y - x}{3x + 6}$.

830. $y' = \dfrac{2x + y}{x - 2y - 5}$.

831. $\begin{cases} \dot{x} = 2x - y, \\ \dot{y} = x - 3 \end{cases}$

832. $\begin{cases} \dot{x} = x + y - 1, \\ \dot{y} = x - y - 3. \end{cases}$

Sketch the integral curves of systems 833-842 in the neighborhood of each singular point. First, state the coordinates of the singular point, and its nature.

833. $y' = \dfrac{6x - y^2 + 1}{2x + y^2 - 1}$.

834. $y' = \dfrac{2y - 2}{4y^2 - x^2}$.

835. $y' = \dfrac{4y^2 - x^2}{2xy - 4y - 8}$.

836. $y' = \dfrac{xy}{4 - 4x - 2y}$.

837. $y' = \dfrac{2y}{x^2 - y^2 - 1}$.

838. $y' = \dfrac{2x}{1 - x^2 - y^2}$.

839. $y' = \dfrac{2x(x - y)}{2 + y - x^2}$.

840. $y' = \dfrac{2xy}{1 - x^2 - y^2}$.

841. $y' = \dfrac{y^2 - x^2}{2(x - 1)(y - 2)}$.

842. $y' = \dfrac{x(2y - x + 5)}{x^2 + y^2 - 6x - 8y}$.

Sketch the integral curves for problems 843-847 in the neighborhood of the origin. Note that in these cases, the singular point is not of the type considered in the discussion at the beginning of this section. Therefore it will be necessary to draw some isoclines. It will also be necessary to determine the limiting directions of the integral curves at the singular points.

843*. $y' = \dfrac{xy}{x+y}.$ **844*.** $y' = \dfrac{x^2+y^2}{x^2+y}.$

845*. $y' = \dfrac{xy}{y+x^2}.$ **846*.** $y' = \dfrac{xy}{y-x^2}.$

847*. $y' = \dfrac{y^2}{y+x^2}.$

848. If the singular point of the curve

$$(ax + by)\, dx + (mx + ny)\, dy = 0$$

is a center, show that the equation is an exact differential. The converse is invalid.

849.* If the equation of the preceding exercise is not exact and has no integrating factor in the neighborhood of the origin, then the singular point is a saddle point.

850.* Suppose that the functions $p(x,y)$, $q(x,y)$ are defined and continuously differentiable in some neighborhood of the origin $(0,0)$, and that each of these functions and each of its first derivatives is 0 at the origin. Show that, if the equation

$$y' = \frac{ax + by + p(x,\ y)}{cx + dy + q(x,\ y)} \tag{10}$$

is unaltered by the substitution $y \to -y$, and if the roots of the characteristic equation

$$\det \begin{bmatrix} c - \lambda, & d \\ a, & b - \lambda \end{bmatrix} = 0$$

are pure imaginaries, then the point $(0,0)$ is a center.

Section 17

PROBLEMS IN THE THEORY OF OSCILLATIONS

Practically all problems in this section are derived from
or based on physical phenomena, and lead to linear equations or
systems with constant coefficients. In case the problems lead
to equations that cannot be solved by use of methods in the
preceding sections, the trajectories should be sketched on the
phase plane, and the particular solution should be tested for
stability.

Problems 862-868, 873 are from the theory of electric cir-
cuits. The following facts are needed. At every point, in particular at every node or junction of a circuit, the sum of the
negative (inflowing) currents is equal to the sum of the positive
(outflowing) currents.

A voltage jump occurs at a device, like a battery or generator,
for producing voltage. In every closed loop of a network, the
algebraic sum of the voltage jumps is equal to the algebraic sum of
the voltage drops. These voltage drops are computed as follows.

The voltage drop across a resistor of R ohms is RI volts, where I is the current in amperes. The voltage drop across an inductor of inductance L henrys is L·dI/dt, where t is the time in seconds. The voltage drop across a capacitor of capacity C farads is q/C, where q = q(t) is the charge in coulombs on the capacitor at time t . Moreover, I = dq/dt, and I = I(t) in the above examples is the current strength flowing through the circuit in question at time t.

Example. The voltage E = V sin wt is applied to a circuit consisting of a resistor of resistance R ohms and a capacitor of capacity C farads in series. Find, as a function of time, the "current neglecting transients," i.e., find the current, assuming that the current is a nonconstant periodic function of the time.

Solution. The explanation above shows that at time t, the current I(t) at each point of the circuit is the same as that at every other point. The voltage drops are RI and q/C through the resistor and capacitor respectively. Therefore the voltage relation

$$RI + q/C = V \sin wt$$

holds. We differentiate this relation with respect to t, and replace dq/dt by I, thus obtaining

$$R \cdot dI/dt + I/C = V \, w \, \cos wt \; . \tag{1}$$

This is the differential equation to solve. It is a linear equation with constant coefficients; examples of this type appear in section 11. It is clear that this equation will have a periodic solution, of the form

$$I(t) = A_1 \cos wt + B_1 \sin wt \; . \tag{2}$$

In fact, if the latter expression is substituted into (1), the constants A_1 and B_1 are easily determined.

However, in electrical engineering, it is customary to write a periodic current in a form that makes its maximum value apparent. Thus we write (2) in the form

$$I = A \sin (wt - \emptyset) \tag{3}$$

which is actually equivalent to (2). After we substitute (3) into (1), we expand the trigonometric functions of wt - ∅ so that only functions of wt and of ∅ appear. Next we collect the terms in sin wt, cos wt and compare coefficients. This yields two equations, as follows

$$RAw \sin \emptyset + (A/C) \cos \emptyset = 0,$$

$$RAw \cos \emptyset - (A/C) \sin \emptyset = Vw$$

Thus we obtain

$$\tan \phi = -1/(RCw), \quad A = \frac{V}{\sqrt{R^2 + \left(\frac{1}{wC}\right)^2}}$$

We have obtained the "current neglecting transients;" this current $I(t)$ is sometimes called the steady-state current. A complete solution of equation (1) is obtained by adding to the function $I(t)$ already obtained the general solution of the homogeneous (reduced) equation

$$R \cdot dI/dt + I/C = 0 . \tag{4}$$

The general solution of (4) is $I = K \exp(-t/RC)$, where K is an arbitrary constant. But for $t \to \infty$ this part of the solution approaches 0 exponentially, and thus every solution of equation (1) approaches the steady state solution; this explains the use of the term.

The above equations for ϕ, A clearly have a geometric interpretation, which is often used in electrical engineering.

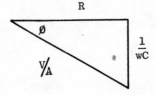

It is important to be able to draw a locus showing the variations of q with I, or of I with dI/dt, the time being a parameter. This locus will be a curve in the (q,I)-plane or in the (I,İ)- plane, See the books by Coddington-Levinson, Lefschetz-LaSalle, Andronow-Chaikin.

Limit cycles. Suppose a trajectory is a closed curve; it therefore represents periodic (or possibly damped deadbeat) motion. If some neighborhood of this closed trajectory consists entirely of trajectories that approach the given trajectory as a limit for $t \to \infty$, the closed trajectory is called a stable limit cycle. If the approach is similar, but for $t \to -\infty$, the closed trajectory is called an unstable limit cycle. If on one side of the trajectory, the trajectories in the neighborhood approach the given trajectory for $t \to \infty$, and on the other side of the given trajectory, the trajectories in the neighborhood approach the given trajectory for $t \to -\infty$, the trajectory is called semistable.

851. A weight of mass m is attached to one end of a spring, and the other end is fixed. The spring constant is k, i.e. if the weight is displaced from equilibrium a distance

x, the spring exerts a force of kx gm. towards equilibrium.
Moreover, if the weight moves with speed v, there is a resistance of nv grams, where n is a constant. At time t = 0,
the weight is placed in the equilibrium position and propelled
with velocity v_o in the direction in which the spring acts.
Find the motion of the weight in the two cases $n^2 < 4$ k m,
$n^2 > 4$ k m.

852.* Suppose that m and k are given in the preceding
problem. Determine n so that the weight reaches its equilibrium position in the shortest possible time (that is, so that
the solution x(t) approaches its equilibrium value as quickly
as possible, t → ∞.

Draw the trajectories for problems 853-859 in the phase
plane. Explain the behavior of the solutions for t → ∞ , by
reference to the sketch, or on the sketch.

853. $\ddot{x} + 4x = 0$.   854. $\ddot{x} - 4\dot{x} + 3x = 0$.
855. $\ddot{x} + 2\dot{x} + 5x = 0$.   856. $\ddot{x} - \dot{x} - 2x = 0$.
857. $2\ddot{x} + 5\dot{x} + 2x = 0$.   858. $\ddot{x} + 2\dot{x} + x = 0$.
859. $\ddot{x} - 2\dot{x} + 2x = 0$.

860. Two pulleys are attached to a shaft; they have moments of inertia I_1, I_2. To twist one of the pulleys an angle ϕ with respect to the other requires an elastic shaft-deforming torque of $K\phi$. Find the frequency of the torsional oscillations of the shaft.

861. A weight of mass m is attached to one end of an elastic rod. The other end moves so that its position at time t has coordinate $B \sin wt$. The elastic force exerted by the rod is proportional to the difference in displacements of its ends. Neglecting the mass of the rod, and friction, find the amplitude A of the forced vibrations of the mass. Can the relation $A > B$ hold?

862. An electric circuit consists of a voltage source that supplies voltage V volts, a resistor of resistance R ohms, and an inductance of L henrys, together with a switch that is closed at time $t = 0$. Find the current as a function of the time.

863. Solve the preceding problem, replacing the inductance L by a capacitor of capacity C farads. The capacitor is uncharged when the switch is closed.

864. A resistor of resistance R ohms is connected to a capacitor of capacity C farads that has a charge q coulombs at time t = 0. The circuit is closed at t = 0. Find the current as a function of time for t > 0.

865. An inductor, resistor, and capacitor are connected in series. At time t = 0, the circuit is closed, the capacitor having a charge of q coulombs at that time. Find the current as a function of time, and the frequency of current change in case the current does actually change sign periodically.

866. A voltage source supplies voltage E = V sin wt in a circuit consisting of the voltage source, and a resistor and capacitor in series. Find the steady-state current in the circuit.

867. A voltage source supplies voltage E = V sin wt and is connected to a resistor, inductor, and capacitor in series. Find the steady-state current in the circuit. What frequency w is needed to obtain the maximum possible current?

868. See figure

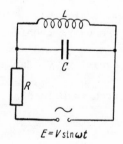

$E = V \sin \omega t$

A voltage source supplies voltage E = V sin wt, through

a resistor of resistance R ohms. The circuit then splits into

two branches consisting of an inductor and capacitor (in paral-

lel), as shown. Find the steady-state current through the

resistor. What frequencies result in non-oscillatory currents?

What frequency results in the least current?

869.* Let the function f(t) have period T, and maxi-

mum value max |f(t)| = m. Find (in the form of a definite

integral) the periodic solution(s) of the equation

$$\ddot{x} + 2 b \dot{x} + x = f(t),$$

and give an upper bound to the amplitude of the periodic solu-

tion(s).

870. A weight of mass m = 2 is attached to a spring like

that of problem 851, with spring constant k = 2. At time

t = 0, the weight is released from position h = 5 above the

equilibrium position, with velocity 0. What is the greatest

excursion of the weight to the other side of the equilibrium

position, if the frictional force f = 1 is independent of the

velocity? Describe the subsequent motion of the weight, and

draw the trajectory in the phase plane.

871. Write the differential equation of motion for a pendulum not acted on by frictional or dissipative forces. Take the case that the values of the coefficients in the equation are all 1, and draw the trajectories in the phase plane. Explain the physical significance of the various types of trajectory.

872. Find the differential equation of motion for a pendulum swinging under resistance proportional to the square of the velocity. Sketch the trajectories on the phase plane.

Hint. Use the sketch from problem 871.

873.

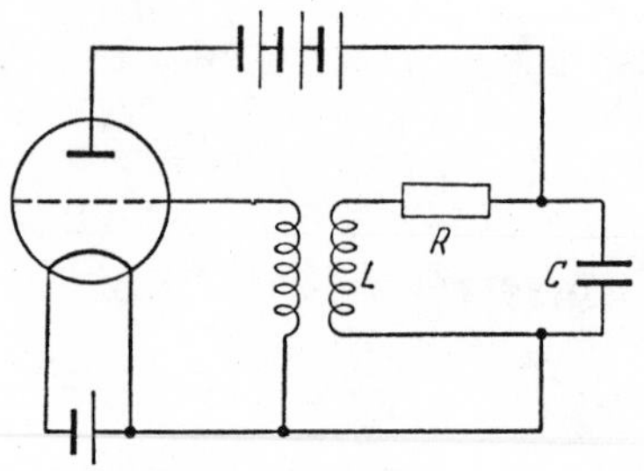

Fig. 6

Give the equation for the amount of current I_L that passes through the capacitor L in a simple oscillating vacuum tube circuit. In the tube, the upper element is the plate or cathode, the central element is the (perforated) grid, and the lower element is the filament or anode. Assume that the plate current I_a (from anode to cathode) is a known function

$I_a = f(v)$ of the voltage V on the grid, and that the function F is given graphically, as in this figure.

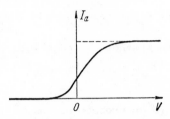

Suppose further that the mutual inductance between the two inductances is M, and that the voltage V is given (to within sign) by the relation

$$V = \pm M \frac{d\,I_L}{dt}.$$

The oscillating circuit in figure 6 contains an inductance, resistance, and capacitance. Under what conditions is the equilibrium condition $I_L(t) = $ const. an unstable condition?

874. Indicate the isoclines, and sketch the trajectories of the equation in problem 873 in the phase plane, in case the equilibrium $I_L = $ const. is unstable. Find the behavior of the solutions for $t \to +\infty$.

Hint. Put the equation into the form

$$\ddot{x} + F(\dot{x}) + x = 0,$$

and sketch the graph of the function F.

In problems 875-884, find the singular points by drawing isoclines and sketching the trajectories in the phase plane. From the sketch, describe the behavior of the solutions for $t \to +\infty$, and state whether periodic solutions of the equation can exist.

The second term in problem 884 is $2^{\dot{x}}$.

875. $\ddot{x} + 2\dot{x} + \dot{x}^2 + x = 0$. **876.** $\ddot{x} - 5\dot{x} - 4x + x^2 = 0$.

877. $2\ddot{x} - \dot{x}^2 - x^2 - 2x = 0$. **878.** $\ddot{x} + \dot{x} + 2x - x^2 = 0$.

879. $\ddot{x} + \dot{x}^2 - x^2 + 1 = 0$. **880.** $2\ddot{x} + \sin x - \sin 2x = 0$.

881. $\ddot{x} + \dot{x}^3 - \dot{x} + x = 0$. **882.** $\ddot{x} + (x^2 - 1)\dot{x} + x = 0$.

883. $\ddot{x} + \dot{x} - 2\operatorname{arctg}\dot{x} + x = 0$.

884. $\ddot{x} + 2^{\dot{x}} - \dot{x} + x = 0$.

Without carrying out the integration to explicit formulas, describe the solutions of equations 885-891, which are given in polar coordinates (r, φ), and determine whether limit cycles exist.

885. $\dfrac{dr}{d\varphi} = r(1 - r^2)$. **886.** $\dfrac{dr}{d\varphi} = r(r - 1)(r - 2)$.

887. $\dfrac{dr}{d\varphi} = r(1 - r)^2$. **888.** $\dfrac{dr}{d\varphi} = \sin r$.

889. $\dfrac{dr}{d\varphi} = (|r - 1| - |r - 2| - 2r + 3)r$.

890. $\dfrac{dr}{d\varphi} = r\sin\dfrac{1}{r}$. **891.** $\dfrac{dr}{d\varphi} = r(1 - r)\sin\dfrac{1}{1-r}$.

892.[*] Determine the values of the constant a for which the system

$$\frac{d\varphi}{dt} = 1, \quad \frac{dr}{dt} = (r - 1)(a + \sin^2\varphi)$$

has stable limit cycles, and the values of a for which it has

unstable limit cycles.

893.* Let f(r) be a continuous function. Determine

conditions under which the system of equations

$$\frac{dr}{dt} = f(r), \quad \frac{d\phi}{dt} = 1,$$

has limit cycles. When will these limit cycles be stable, un-

stable, semistable?

894.* Let F(z) be a continuous function of z with the

properties that, for $z > 0$ the relation $F(z) > F(0)$ holds,

and for $z < 0$ the relation $F(z) < F(0)$ holds. Show that the

equation

$$\ddot{x} + F(\dot{x}) + x = 0$$

cannot have a limit cycle (in the phase plane).

Section 18

DEPENDENCE OF SOLUTIONS ON INITIAL CONDITIONS
AND ON PARAMETERS

APPROXIMATE SOLUTION OF DIFFERENTIAL EQUATIONS

Let $x_1(t), \ldots, x_n(t)$ be the solution of the system

$$dx_i/dt = f_i(t, x_1, \ldots, x_n), \quad i = 1, \ldots, n, \tag{1}$$

where all the functions f_i are differentiable and the relations

$\left| \partial f_i / \partial x_j \right| \leq K$ hold for $i, j = 1, \ldots, n$. Suppose that the func-

tions $y_1(t), \ldots, y_n(t)$ are functions that satisfy the inequali-

ties

$$\left| dy_i/dt - f_i(t, y_1, \ldots, y_n) \right| \leq \eta_i, \quad i = 1, \ldots, n, \tag{2}$$

$$\left| y_i(0) - x_i(0) \right| \leq \delta_i, \quad i = 1, \ldots, n. \tag{3}$$

Then the estimate below holds.

$$\sum_{i=1}^{n} \left| x_i(t) - y_i(t) \right| \leq \delta \, e^{Kn \left| t \right|} + [\eta/Kn] \, (e^{Kn \left| t \right|} - 1)$$

where $\delta = \delta_1 + \cdots + \delta_n$, $\eta = \eta_1 + \cdots + \eta_n$.

This latter inequality can be used to estimate the degree

with which the functions $y_1, \ldots, y_n$ approximate a solution of

the system (1), and also the difference between a solution of

the system (1) and the system

$$dy_i/dt = g_i(t, y_1, \ldots, y_n), \quad i = 1, \ldots, n,$$

if it is known that the relations $\left| g_i - f_i \right| \leq \eta_i$ **hold** for

$i = 1, \ldots, n.$

We now consider the system

$$dx_i/dt = f_i(t, x_1, \ldots, x_n, \mu), \quad i = 1, \ldots, n \qquad (4)$$

which involves a parameter μ and which is to be solved subject

to the initial conditions

$$x_i(0) = a_i(\mu), \quad i = 1, \ldots, n \qquad (5)$$

where the parameter μ usually takes on values which do not

vary greatly from a neutral value, and the functions f_i, a_i

are continuous for $i = 1, \ldots, n,$ and have continuous derivatives

with respect to $x_1, \ldots, x_n, \mu$. The hypotheses just stated

insure that the solution of (4) will be a continuously differ-

entiable function of the parameter μ. The derivative

$\partial x_i/\partial \mu = u_i,$ satisfies the linear system of equations

$$du_i/dt = \sum_{j=1}^{n} (\partial f_i/\partial x_j) u_j + \partial f_i/\partial \mu, \quad i = 1, \ldots, n, \qquad (6)$$

subject to the initial conditions

$$u_i(0) = a_i'(\mu), \quad i = 1, \ldots, n.$$

In formula (6) the values of the derivatives $\partial f_i/\partial x_j$, $\partial f_i/\partial \mu$

are to be computed for $x_1 = x_1(t), \ldots, x_n(t),$ where the functions represent a solution of system (4) subject to the initial conditions (5).

In particular if the initial conditions are taken in the form $a_k(\mu) = \mu$, $a_i(\mu) = $ const for values of $i \neq k$, and if we assume that all the functions $f_1, \ldots, f_n$ are independent of μ, the assertion above can be particularized. It states in this case that the system (4), subject to the initial conditions $x_i(0) = a_i(\mu)$, $i = 1, \ldots, k, \ldots, n$ will have a solution that varies with the initial condition as follows. The derivative $\partial x_i / \partial a_k = u_i$ of the arbitrary component x_i with respect to the initial value a_k is obtainable from the formula

$$du_i/dt = \sum_{j=1}^{n} \partial f_i / \partial x_j, \quad i = 1, \ldots, n.$$

The initial conditions for the latter equation are $u_i(0) = 0$ for $i \neq k$, $u_k(0) = 1$.

895. The equation $y' = x + \sin y$ is to be solved on the interval $(0, 1)$ subject to the initial condition $y(0) = y_o = 0$. If y_o is perturbed by 0.01, estimate the maximum variation of the solution on this interval.

896. The equation $\ddot{x} + \sin x = 0$ is to be solved on the interval $0 \leq t \leq T$ subject to the initial conditions

$x(0) = 0$, $\dot{x}(0) = 0$. If the right member is replaced by a function $\phi(t)$ that has absolute value ≤ 0.1, $|\phi(t)| \leq 0.1$, how much will the solution be perturbed? The question concerns the action of a small perturbing force.

897. The system $\dot{x} = x-y$, $\dot{y} = tx$ is to be solved for the initial conditions $x(0) = 1$, $y(0) = 0$, on the interval $|t| \leq 0.1$. Find the maximum error in the solution

$$\tilde{x}(t) = 1 + t + \frac{1}{2} t^2, \quad \tilde{y}(t) = \frac{1}{2} t^2.$$

898. The equation $y'' - x^2 y = 0$ is to be solved on the interval $|x| \leq 0.5$, subject to the initial conditions $y(0) = 1$, $y'(0) = 0$. Find the error in using the approximate solution

$$\tilde{y}(x) = \exp(x^4/12).$$

899.[*] Answer the same question for the differential equation $y' = 2x y^2 + 1$ on the interval $|x| \leq 0.25$ subject to the initial condition $y(0) = 1$ for the solution

$$\tilde{y}(x) = (1-x)^{-1}.$$

In problems 900-902 find the indicated derivative with respect to the parameter or with respect to the initial condition.

900. $y' = y + \mu(x + y^2)$, $y(0) = 1$; find $\left.\dfrac{\partial y}{\partial \mu}\right|_{\mu=0}$.

901. $\begin{cases} \dot{x} = xy + t^2 \\ 2\dot{y} = -y^2 \end{cases}$ $x(1) = x_0 = 3$, $y(1) = y_0 = 2$; find $\dfrac{\partial x}{\partial y_0}$.

902. $\ddot{x} - \dot{x} = (x+1)^2 - \mu x^2$; $x(0) = \dfrac{1}{2}$, $\dot{x}(0) = -1$;

find $\left.\dfrac{\partial x}{\partial \mu}\right|_{\mu=1}$.

903. * Suppose the differential equation $\ddot{x} = f(t,x,\dot{x})$ has a solution on the interval $0 \le t \le T$ subject to the initial conditions $x(0) = a$, $\dot{x}(0) = b$. Suppose further that the function $f(t,x,y)$ has continuous derivatives, and that $\partial f/\partial x \ge 0$. Demonstrate that on the entire t - interval, the derivative of the solution with respect to the initial value b is positive.

904. * Suppose the system of differential equations

$$dx_i/dt = f_i(t, x_1, \ldots x_n), \quad i = 1, \ldots, n$$

has a solution for $t \ge t_0$ subject to the initial conditions $x_i(t_0) = x_{io}$. Suppose further that the functions f_i and the partial derivatives $\partial f_i/\partial x_k$ are continuous and that the inequalities $|\partial f_0/\partial x_k| \le L(t)$, hold for $i, k = 1, \ldots, n$.

Establish the inequalities

$$|\partial x_i/\partial x_{k0}| \le \exp n \int_{t_0}^{t} L(s)\, ds, \quad i, k = 1, \ldots, n.$$

Use the method of small parameters in problems 905-914 to find a periodic function which is an approximate solution of the given equations. If the right member is a periodic function

of t, the solution must have the same period as the right mem-

ber. The symbol μ is a small parameter. The method desired is

explained in the book of Coddington and Levinson.

905. $\ddot{x} + 3x = 2\sin t + \mu\dot{x}^2$.   **906.** $\ddot{x} + 5x = \cos 2t + \mu x^2$.

907. $\ddot{x} + 3x + x^3 = 2\mu\cos t$.   **908.** $\ddot{x} + x^2 = 1 + \mu\sin t$.

909. $\ddot{x} + \sin x = \mu\sin 2t$.

910. $\ddot{x} + x = \sin 3t - \sin 2t + \mu\ x^2$;   only find the zeroth
approximation.

911*. $\ddot{x} + x = 6\mu\sin t - x^3$.   **912.** $\ddot{x} + x - x^2 = 0$.

913. $\ddot{x} + \sin x = 0$.   **914.** $\ddot{x} + x = \mu(1 - x^2)\dot{x}$.

Use Adam's or Störmer's method in problems 915-917 to ob-

tain an approximate solution of the equations on the interval

indicated. Carry three decimal places (accuracy of 0.001). Use

a power series to obtain starting values. Descriptions of the

methods of approximate calculation are to be found in books on

numerical analysis, e.g. Hildebrand, F.B. Introduction to numer-

ical analysis, New York: McGraw-Hill, 1956, p. 198; Collatz, L.

Numerische Behandlung von Differentialgleichungen, Berlin:

Springer, 1955, pp. 79, 81, 499.

915. $y' = y$, $y(0) = 1$; $0 \leqslant x \leqslant 1$.

916. $y' = y^2 - x$, $y(0) = 0.5$; $0 \leqslant x \leqslant 1$.

917. $xy'' + y' + xy = 0$, $y(0) = 1$, $y'(0) = 0$; $0 \leqslant x \leqslant 1$.

Problems 918-920 can be solved by equating the slope of the direction field attached to the equation $y' = f(x,y)$ with the slope of appropriately chosen curves $y = \phi_i(x)$.

918. Show that the solution of the equation $y' = x - y^2$ that satisfies the initial condition $y(4) = 2$ satisfies the inequalities $\sqrt{x} - 0.07 < y(x) < \sqrt{x}$ for all positive values of x exceeding 4, $4 < x$.

919.* Show that the solution $y(x)$ of the equation $y' = x - y^2$ that satisfies the initial condition $y(x_o) = y_o$, $x_o \geq 0$, $y_o \geq 0$ satisfies the relation $y(x) - \sqrt{x} \to 0$ for $x \to \infty$.

920.* Give upper and lower estimates for the periodic solution of the equation

$$y' = 2y^2 - \cos^2 5x,$$

that lies in the region $y < 0$.

Section 19

NON-LINEAR SYSTEMS

By an appropriate elimination process, a system of differential equations can be reduced to a single equation in one
unknown or to several equations with one unknown function in
each equation. This is a purely algebraic process, at least
in principle.

Example 1. Solve the system of equations

$$y' = \frac{z}{x}, \quad z' = \frac{(y - z)^2 + xz}{x^2}. \tag{1}$$

Solution: To eliminate z from the given system we proceed as follows. From the first equation we find $z = xy'$.
Substituting this in the second equation we obtain the following relation.

$$x^3 y'' = (y - xy')^2$$

The given system of equations has been replaced by a single
second order equation. A possible way to solve this equation
is explained in section 10, "Reduction of the Order of an
Equation." Once this equation has been solved for y, the
value of z can be found from the relation $z = xy'$.

If we use this method on most systems of equations the resulting equation in a single unknown usually has very high order. It is therefore more convenient as a rule to attempt to find a combination of the variables which gives an integral of the system. Such a combination is called a first integral.

Example 2. Solve the following system in symmetric form (it is always possible to bring a system into symmetric form by introducing a sufficient number of extra variables)

$$\frac{dx}{xz} = \frac{dy}{yz} = \frac{dz}{-xy}.$$
(2)

The first equality of this set is an integrable combination. If we simply multiply both sides of this first equality by z and integrate we obtain the following first integral:

$$\frac{x}{y} = C_1$$
(3)

A second integrable combination is obtained by using the following assertion. If the relations

$$\frac{a_1}{b_1} = \frac{a_2}{b_2} = \ldots = \frac{a_n}{b_n} = t,$$

hold, then the following relation will hold for arbitrary values of $k_1, k_2, \cdots, k_n$:

$$\frac{k_1 a_1 + k_2 a_2 + \ldots + k_n a_n}{k_1 b_1 + k_2 b_2 + \ldots + k_n b_n} = t.$$

This assertion allows us to obtain from (2)

$$\frac{y \cdot dx + x \cdot dy}{y \cdot xz + x \cdot yz} = \frac{dz}{-xy}; \quad \frac{d(xy)}{2xyz} = \frac{dz}{-xy}; \quad d(xy) = -2z \, dz.$$

thus we obtain another integral

$$xy + z^2 = C_2. \tag{4}$$

Obviously the two integrals (3) and (4) are independent and the system has been solved.

It would have been possible to proceed in the following alternative manner. By using the first integral (3) we could eliminate the unknown x in the second equation of (2). Indeed, if we substitute $x = C_1 y$ in this second equation, we obtain

$$\frac{dy}{yz} = \frac{dz}{-C_1 y^2} .$$

But this is an integrable equation, indeed the variables are separable: $-C_1 y \, dy = z \, dz; \quad z^2 = -C_1 y^2 + C_2.$

The last step is to replace C_1 by its value from formula (3), and thus we get another first integral:

$$z^2 + xy = C_2$$

Solve the given systems of equations 921-940.

921. $y' = \dfrac{x}{z}$, $z' = -\dfrac{x}{y}$.   **922.** $y' = \dfrac{y^2}{z-x}$, $z' = y+1$.

923. $y' = \dfrac{z}{x}$, $z' = \dfrac{z(y+2z-1)}{x(y-1)}$.   **924.** $y' = y^2 z$, $z' = \dfrac{z}{x} - yz^2$.

925. $2zy' = y^2 - z^2 + 1$, $z' = z+y$.   **926.** $\dfrac{dx}{2y-z} = \dfrac{dy}{y} = \dfrac{dz}{z}$.

927. $\dfrac{dx}{y} = \dfrac{dy}{x} = \dfrac{dz}{z}$.   **928.** $\dfrac{dx}{y+z} = \dfrac{dy}{x+z} = \dfrac{dz}{x+y}$.

929. $\dfrac{dx}{y-x} = \dfrac{dy}{x+y+z} = \dfrac{dz}{x-y}$.   **930.** $\dfrac{dx}{z} = \dfrac{dy}{u} = \dfrac{dz}{x} = \dfrac{du}{y}$.

931. $\dfrac{dx}{y-u} = \dfrac{dy}{z-x} = \dfrac{dz}{u-y} = \dfrac{du}{x-z}$.

932. $\dfrac{dx}{z} = \dfrac{dy}{xz} = \dfrac{dz}{y}$.   **933.** $\dfrac{dx}{z^2 - y^2} = \dfrac{dy}{z} = -\dfrac{dz}{y}$.

934. $\dfrac{dx}{x} = \dfrac{dy}{y} = \dfrac{dz}{xy+z}$.   **935.** $\dfrac{dx}{xz} = \dfrac{dy}{yz} = \dfrac{dz}{xy\sqrt{z^2+1}}$.

936. $\dfrac{dx}{x+y^2+z^2} = \dfrac{dy}{y} = \dfrac{dz}{z}$.

937. $\dfrac{dx}{x(y+z)} = \dfrac{dy}{z(z-y)} = \dfrac{dz}{y(y-z)}$.

938. $-\dfrac{dx}{x^2} = \dfrac{dy}{xy-2z^2} = \dfrac{dz}{xz}$.

939. $\dfrac{dx}{x(z-y)} = \dfrac{dy}{y(y-x)} = \dfrac{dz}{y^2 - xz}$.

940. $\dfrac{dx}{x(y^2-z^2)} = -\dfrac{dy}{y(z^2+x^2)} = \dfrac{dz}{z(x^2+y^2)}$.

In problems 941-943 the functions ϕ are testing functions from which you must determine whether $\phi = C$ is a first integral of the system beside which it stands.

941. $\dfrac{dx}{dt} = \dfrac{x^2 - t}{y}$, $\dfrac{dy}{dt} = -x$; $\varphi_1 = t^2 + 2xy$; $\varphi_2 = x^2 - ty$.

942. $\dot{x} = xy$, $\dot{y} = x^2 + y^2$; $\varphi_1 = x \ln y - x^2 y$; $\varphi_2 = \dfrac{y^2}{x^2} - 2 \ln x$.

943. $\dfrac{dx}{y} = -\dfrac{dy}{x} = \dfrac{dz}{u} = -\dfrac{du}{z}$; $\varphi = yz - ux$.

944. Determine whether the two first integrals

$$\frac{x + y}{z + x} = C_1 , \quad \frac{z - y}{x + y} = C_2$$

of the system

$$\frac{dx}{x} = \frac{dy}{y} = \frac{dz}{z} .$$

are independent.

945.* Let $\phi(x,y)$ be a continuous function of x and y,

and suppose that the origin is a singular point, in fact is

either a node or a focus of the system

$$dx/dt = P(x,y), \quad dy/dt = Q(x,y).$$

Show that $\phi(x,y) = C$ cannot be a first integral of the system.

Section 20

FIRST ORDER PARTIAL DIFFERENTIAL EQUATIONS

Let $a_1, \ldots, a_n$, b be functions of $x_1, \ldots x_n$, z

To solve the first order differential equation

$$a_1 \frac{\partial z}{\partial x} + \ldots + a_n \frac{\partial z}{\partial x_n} = b, \tag{1}$$

It is necessary to solve the following symmetric system of first order differential equations

$$\frac{dx_1}{a_1} = \ldots = \frac{dx_n}{a_n} = \frac{dz}{b} \tag{2}$$

indeed to find n independent first integrals of this system:

$$\phi_1 (x_1, \ldots, x_n, z) = C_1$$

$$\phi_n(x_1, \ldots, x_n, z) = C_n. \tag{3}$$

If these integrals can be found, then every solution of system (1) can be written in the form

$$F (\phi_1, \ldots, \phi_n) = 0, \tag{4}$$

where F is an arbitrary differentiable function.

In particular, suppose z occurs explicitly in just one of the first integrals (3) for example, in the last one. Then if F is an arbitrary differentiable function the general solu-

tion can be written in the form

$$\phi_n (x_1, \ldots, x_n, z) = f (\phi_1, \ldots, \phi_{n-1}). \tag{5}$$

If we then solve (5) for z, we obtain the general solution of

(1) in explicit form.

Suppose we wish to find a surface $z = z(x,y)$ that satis-

fies the differential equation

$$a_1 (x, y, z)\frac{\partial z}{\partial x} + a_2 (x, y, z)\frac{\partial z}{\partial y} = b (x, y, z) \tag{6}$$

and that goes through a given curve

$$x = u(t), \quad y = v(t), z = w(t). \tag{7}$$

The following procedure will be successful. We first find two

independent first integrals of the system

$$\frac{dx}{a_1} = \frac{dy}{a_2} = \frac{dz}{b}. \tag{8}$$

Suppose these are

$$\phi_1 (x, y, z) = C_1, \quad \phi_2(x, y, z) = C_2 \tag{9}$$

In these latter equations we replace x,y,z by their values from

equation (7) and obtain in this way two equations in the param-

eter t:

$$\vartheta_1 (t) = C_1, \quad \vartheta_2 (t) = C_2 \tag{10}$$

We now eliminate t and obtain a relation of the following form:

$$F\ (C_1,\ C_2) = 0.$$

Finally we replace C_1, C_2 by the functions ϕ_1, ϕ_2 from the left members of the integrals (9), and have a surface of the required type.

If it happens that the two equations (10) are independent of t, it must be true that the curve (7) lies on every solution of the system (6), that is, it is a characteristic of this system. In this case the Cauchy problem has infinitely many solutions.

Example. Find the general solution of the equation

$$xz\ \partial z/\partial\ x + yz\ \partial z/\partial y = -xy \tag{11}$$

and find a surface which contains the curve

$$y = x^2,\ z = x^3 \tag{12}$$

Solution: The system of equations to be solved is

$$\frac{dx}{xz} = \frac{dy}{yz} = \frac{dz}{-xy}$$

for which two first integrals were found in section 19:

$$\frac{x}{y} = C_1,\ z^2 + xy = C_2 \tag{13}$$

Therefore, the general solution of (11) can be written in the form

$$F\left(\frac{x}{y},\ z^2 + xy\right) = 0,$$

where F is an arbitrary function. Since z is absent from one of the first integrals, the general solution can also be written in explicit form as follows:

$$z^2 + xy = f\left(\frac{x}{y}\right); \quad z = \pm\sqrt{f\left(\frac{x}{y}\right) - xy}$$

Here f is an arbitrary function.

To find the integral surface which contains the curve (12) we must first write the equations of this curve in parametric form:

$$x = x, \quad y = x^2, \quad z = x^3.$$

We now substitute this in (13) and obtain

$$1/x = C_1, \quad x^6 + x^3 = C_2 .$$

x can be eliminated as follows:

$$\frac{1}{C_1^6} + \frac{1}{C_1^3} = C_2 .$$

In this latter equation C_1 and C_2 stand for expressions in the system (13) and thus the integral surface required is:

$$\left(\frac{y}{x}\right)^6 + \left(\frac{y}{x}\right)^3 = z^2 + xy.$$

124

Find the general solution for problems 946-963.

946. $y \dfrac{\partial z}{\partial x} + x \dfrac{\partial z}{\partial y} = x - y.$ **947.** $e^x \dfrac{\partial z}{\partial x} + y^2 \dfrac{\partial z}{\partial y} = y e^x.$

948. $2x \dfrac{\partial z}{\partial x} + (y - x) \dfrac{dz}{\partial y} - x^2 = 0.$

949. $xy \dfrac{\partial z}{\partial x} - x^2 \dfrac{\partial z}{\partial y} = yz.$

950. $x \dfrac{\partial z}{\partial x} + 2y \dfrac{\partial z}{\partial y} = x^2 y + z.$

951. $(x^2 + y^2) \dfrac{\partial z}{\partial x} + 2xy \dfrac{\partial z}{\partial y} + z^2 = 0.$

952. $2y^4 \dfrac{\partial z}{\partial x} - xy \dfrac{\partial z}{\partial y} = x \sqrt{z^2 + 1}.$

953. $x^2 z \dfrac{\partial z}{\partial x} + y^2 z \dfrac{\partial z}{\partial y} = x + y.$

954. $yz \dfrac{\partial z}{\partial x} - xz \dfrac{\partial z}{\partial y} = e^z.$

955. $(z - y)^2 \dfrac{\partial z}{\partial x} + xz \dfrac{\partial z}{\partial y} = xy.$

956. $xy \dfrac{\partial z}{\partial x} + (x - 2z) \dfrac{\partial z}{\partial y} = yz.$

957. $y \dfrac{\partial z}{\partial x} + z \dfrac{\partial z}{\partial y} = \dfrac{y}{x}.$

958. $\sin^2 x \dfrac{\partial z}{\partial x} + \operatorname{tg} z \dfrac{\partial z}{\partial y} = \cos^2 z.$

959. $(x + z) \dfrac{\partial z}{\partial x} + (y + z) \dfrac{\partial z}{\partial y} = x + y.$

960. $(xz + y) \dfrac{\partial z}{\partial x} + (x + yz) \dfrac{\partial z}{\partial y} = 1 - z^2.$

961. $(y + z) \dfrac{\partial u}{\partial x} + (z + x) \dfrac{\partial u}{\partial y} + (x + y) \dfrac{\partial u}{\partial z} = u.$

962. $x \dfrac{\partial u}{\partial x} + y \dfrac{\partial u}{\partial y} + (z + u) \dfrac{\partial u}{\partial z} = xy.$

963. $(u - x) \dfrac{\partial u}{\partial x} + (u - y) \dfrac{\partial u}{\partial y} - z \dfrac{\partial u}{\partial z} = x + y.$

In problems 964-980 find the surface which satisfies the differential equation in question and contains the given curve.

964. $y^2 \dfrac{\partial z}{\partial x} + xy \dfrac{\partial z}{\partial y} = x$; $\quad x = 0$, $\quad z = y^2$.

965. $x \dfrac{\partial z}{\partial x} - 2y \dfrac{\partial z}{\partial y} = x^2 + y^2$; $\quad y = 1$, $\quad z = x^2$.

966. $x \dfrac{\partial z}{\partial x} + y \dfrac{\partial z}{\partial y} = z - xy$; $\quad x = 2$, $\quad z = y^2 + 1$.

967. $\operatorname{tg} x \dfrac{\partial z}{\partial x} + y \dfrac{\partial z}{\partial y} = z$; $\quad y = x$, $\quad z = x^3$.

968. $x \dfrac{\partial z}{\partial x} - y \dfrac{\partial z}{\partial y} = z^2 (x - 3y)$; $\quad x = 1$, $\quad yz + 1 = 0$.

969. $x \dfrac{\partial z}{\partial x} + y \dfrac{\partial z}{\partial y} = z - x^2 - y^2$; $\quad y = -2$, $\quad z = x - x^2$.

970. $yz \dfrac{\partial z}{\partial x} + xz \dfrac{\partial z}{\partial y} = xy$; $\quad x = a$, $\quad y^2 + z^2 = a^2$.

971. $z \dfrac{\partial z}{\partial x} - xy \dfrac{\partial z}{\partial y} = 2xz$; $\quad x + y = 2$, $\quad yz = 1$.

972. $z \dfrac{\partial z}{\partial x} + (z^2 - x^2) \dfrac{\partial z}{\partial y} + x = 0$; $\quad y = x^2$, $\quad z = 2x$.

973. $(y - z) \dfrac{\partial z}{\partial x} + (z - x) \dfrac{\partial z}{\partial y} = x - y$; $\quad z = y = -x$.

974. $x \dfrac{\partial z}{\partial x} + (xz + y) \dfrac{\partial z}{\partial y} = z$; $\quad x + y = 2z$, $\quad xz = 1$.

975. $y^2 \dfrac{\partial z}{\partial x} + yz \dfrac{\partial z}{\partial y} + z^2 = 0$; $\quad x - y = 0$, $\quad x - yz = 1$.

976. $x \dfrac{\partial z}{\partial x} + z \dfrac{\partial z}{\partial y} = y$; $\quad y = 2z$, $\quad x + 2y = z$.

977. $(y + 2z^2) \dfrac{\partial z}{\partial x} - 2x^2 z \dfrac{\partial z}{\partial y} = x^2$; $\quad x = z$, $\quad y = x^2$.

978. $(x - z) \dfrac{\partial z}{\partial x} + (y - z) \dfrac{\partial z}{\partial y} = 2z$; $\quad x - y = 2$, $\quad z + 2x = 1$.

979. $xy^3 \dfrac{\partial z}{\partial x} + x^2 z^2 \dfrac{\partial z}{\partial y} = y^3 z$; $\quad x = -z^3$, $\quad y = z^2$.

980*. $x \dfrac{\partial z}{\partial x} + y \dfrac{\partial z}{\partial y} = 2xy$; $\quad y = x$, $\quad z = x^2$.

981. Find the general equation of the surfaces which inter-- sect the surfaces of the family $z^2 = Cxy$ orthogonally.

982. Find the equation of a surface which contains the line

$$y = x, \ z = 1 \quad \text{and is orthogonal to the}$$

surfaces

$$x^2 + y^2 + z^2 = Cx.$$

983. Find the partial differential equation that is satisfied by cylindrical surfaces with elements parallel to the vector $[1,1,2]$. State the general solution of this equation.

984. Use the result of the preceding problem to find the equation of a cylindrical surface with elements parallel to the vector $[1,1,2]$, given that its generating curve is

$$x + y + z = 0, \ 5x^2 + 6xy + 5y^2 = 4.$$

985. Set up and solve the partial differential equation that is satisfied by all conical surfaces with vertex in a fixed point (a,b,c).

986. Find the equation of the family of surfaces with the following property: The abscissa of the point of intersection of an arbitrary tangent plane with the x-axis is half as great as the abscissa of the point of tangency.

In problems 987-989 solve the given system of equations.

987. $\begin{cases} \dfrac{\partial z}{\partial x} = \dfrac{z}{x}, \\ \dfrac{\partial z}{\partial y} = \dfrac{2z}{y}. \end{cases}$
988. $\begin{cases} \dfrac{\partial z}{\partial x} = y - z, \\ \dfrac{\partial z}{\partial y} = xz. \end{cases}$

989. $\begin{cases} \dfrac{\partial z}{\partial x} = 2yz - z^2, \\ \dfrac{\partial z}{\partial y} = xz. \end{cases}$

The problem of Pfaff is to be solved by rewriting the differential equation so that it becomes exact. This leads to partial differential equations for the intergrating factor; the latter are to be solved by the methods already explained.

In problems 990-993 find the surface which satisfies the given Pfaffian condition.

990. $(x - y) dx + z dy - x dz = 0.$
991. $3yz dx + 2xz dy + xy dz = 0.$
992. $(z + xy) dx - (z + y^2) dy + y dz = 0.$
993. $(2yz + 3x) dx + xz dy + xy dz = 0.$

ANSWERS

Note. In all places, even where not so indicated, the arguments of logarithms are absolute values. The answer $x = C_1 \exp y$ is sometimes written $y = LN\ Cx$, without any requirement that C and x have the same sign. The precise form would be $y = LN\ |Cx|$. In some cases, printing difficulties have required the omission of the absolute value sign, but it <u>must</u> be understood when needed. Only when the argument of the logarithm is necessarily positive for all allowable real values of the variables can the symbol be omitted.

1. Isoclines, Construction of the Differential Equation for a Family of Curves Isogonal Trajectories

15. $f(x, y) = 0$; $f'_x < 0$ (max), $f'_x > 0$ (min). 16. $f'_x + f \cdot f'_y = 0$.

17. $y = e^{\frac{xy'}{y}}$. 18. $y' = 3y^{\frac{2}{3}}$. 19. $xy' = 3y$. 20. $y^2 + y'^2 = 1$.

21. $x^2 y' - xy = yy'$. 22. $2xyy' - y^2 = 2x^3$. 23. $y'^3 = 4y(xy' - 2y)$.

24. $y' = \cos \dfrac{x\sqrt{1 - y'^2}}{y}$. 25. $x(x-2)y'' - (x^2-2)y' + 2(x-1)y = 0$.

26. $(yy'' + y'^2)^2 = -y^3 y''$. 27. $(1 - x\operatorname{ctg} x)y'' - xy' + y = 0$.

28. $x^3 y''' - 3x^2 y'' + 6xy' - 6y - 0$. 29. $y''' y' = 3y''^2$.

30. $(y - 2x)^2(y'^2 + 1) = (2y'^2 + 1)^2$. 31. $xy'^2 = y(2y' - 1)$.

32. $[x - y(\sqrt{2} + 1)]^2 (y'^2 + 1) = (x + yy')^2$. 33. $x^2 y'' - 2xy' + 2y = 0$.

34. $(y''y + y'^2 + 1)^2 = (y'^2 + 1)^3$. 35. $yy' + zz' = 0$, $y^2 + 2xzz' = x^2 z'^2$.

36. $x^2 + y^2 = z^2 - 2z(y - xy')$; $x + yy' = zz' - z'(y - xy')$.

37. $4yy' = -x$. 38. $y' = -2y$. 39. $(x^2 + y)y' = -x$.

40. $(x + y)y' = y - x$; $(x - y)y' = x + y$. 41. $(x \mp y\sqrt{3})y' = y \pm x\sqrt{3}$. 42. $(3x \mp y\sqrt{3})y' = y \pm 3x\sqrt{3}$. 43. $(2x \mp y\sqrt{3})y' = y \pm 2x\sqrt{3}$. 44. $r' \sin\theta = r^2$. 45. $r' = \dfrac{1}{2}r\operatorname{ctg}\theta$. 46. $r' = r\operatorname{ctg}(\theta \pm 45°)$.

47. $(x + 2y)y' = -3x - y$; $(3x + 2y)y' = y - x$. 48. $y'[2xy \pm (x^2 - y^2)] = y^2 - x^2 \pm 2xy$. 49. $x(1 + y'^2) = -2yy'$. 50. $yy'^3 + xy'^2 = -1$.

2. Equations in which the Variables are Separable.

51. $y = C(x+1)e^{-x}$; $x = -1$. **52.** $\ln|x| = C + \sqrt{y^2+1}$.
53. $y(\ln|x^2-1|+C) = 1$, $y = 0$; $y[\ln(1-x^2)+1] = 1$.
54. $y = 2 + C\cos x$; $y = 2 - 3\cos x$.   **55.** $y = (x-C)^3$; $y = 0$;
$y = (x-2)^3$; $y = 0$.   **56.** $y(1-Cx) = 1$; $y = 0$; $y(1+x) = 1$.

57. $y^2 - 2 = Ce^{\frac{1}{x}}$. **58.** $(Ce^{-x^2}-1)y = 2$; $y = 0$. **59.** $e^{-s} = 1 + Ce^t$.
60. $z = -\lg(C-10^x)$. **61.** $x^2+t^2-2t = C$. **62.** $\operatorname{ctg}\dfrac{y-x}{2} = x+C$;
$y - x = 2\pi k$, $k = 0$, ± 1, ± 2, ...   **63.** $2x+y-1 = Ce^x$.

64. $x+2y+2 = Ce^y$; $x+2y+2 = 0$.   **65.** $\sqrt{4x+2y-1} -$
$- 2\ln(\sqrt{4x+2y-1}+2) = x+C$.   **66.** $y = \operatorname{arctg}\left(1-\dfrac{2}{x}\right)+2\pi$.
67. $y = 2$. **68.** a) $2y^2+x^2 = C$; b) $y^2+2x = C$; c) $y^2 = Ce^{x^2+y^2}$.

3. Geometrical and Physical Problems.

71. $(C \pm x)\, y = 2a^2$. **72.** $b \ln y - y = \pm x + C$, $0 < y < b$.

73. $a \ln(a \pm \sqrt{a^2 - y^2}) \mp \sqrt{a^2 - y^2} = x + C$. **74.** $y = Cx^2$. **75.** $y = Cx^2$.

76. $r(1 \pm \cos\phi) = C$. **77.** 10 min. **78.** 0.5 kg. **79.** 24 min.

80. 40 min. **81.** 7.8 min. **82.** $b - \dfrac{b-a}{60\,k}(1 - e^{-60k})$.

83. 50 sec. 15 m. **84.** 200 days. **85.** 1575 years. **86.** 975.10^6

year. **87.** 98.1%. **88.** 23 sec. **89.** 1.75 sec,, 16.3 m, 2 sec.,

20 m. **90.** 1.87 sec., 16.4 m/sec. **91.** 17.5 min. **92.** 17.3 min.

93. $5(2 + \sqrt{2}) = 17.07$ min. **94.** 27 sec. **95.** 260 sec., 200 sec.

96. 0.5 kP. **97.** $p = \exp(-0.12h)$, where p is measured in

kg/cm^2, and h is measured in km. **98.** 5350 kg.

99. $m_o - v(q_1 - q_o)(1 - e^{-kt})$, where k is the coefficient of

proportionality. **100.** $c \ln(M/m)$.

4. Homogeneous Equations.

101. $x + y = Cx^2$; $x = 0$.　　**102.** $\ln(x^2 + y^2) = C - 2\,\text{arctg}\,\dfrac{y}{x}$.

103. $x(y-x) = Cy$; $y = 0$. **104.** $x = \pm\, y\,\sqrt{\ln Cx}$; $y = 0$. **105.** $y = Ce^{\frac{y}{x}}$.

106. $y^2 - x^2 = Cy$, $y = 0$.　**107.** $\sin\dfrac{y}{x} = Cx$.　**108.** $y = -x\ln\ln Cx$.

109. $\ln\dfrac{x+y}{x} = Cx$.　**110.** $\ln Cx = \text{ctg}\left(\dfrac{1}{2}\ln\dfrac{y}{x}\right)$; $\; y = xe^{2\pi k}, \;\; k = 0,$

$\pm 1, \pm 2, \ldots$ **111.** $x\ln Cx = 2\sqrt{xy}$; $y = 0$. **112.** $\arcsin\dfrac{y}{x} = \ln Cx\cdot\text{sgn}\,x$;

$y = \pm x$. **113.** $(y-2x)^3 = C(y-x-1)^2$; $y = x+1$. **114.** $2x+y-1 = Ce^{2y-x}$.
115. $(y-x+2)^2 + 2x = C$.　　**116.** $(y-x+5)^5(x+2y-2) = C$.

117. $(y+2)^2 = C(x+y-1)$; $y = 1 - x$. **118.** $y + 2 = Ce^{-2\,\text{arctg}\,\frac{y+2}{x-3}}$.

119. $\ln\dfrac{y+x}{x+3} = 1 + \dfrac{C}{x+y}$.　　　**120.** $\sin\dfrac{y-2x}{x+1} = C(x+1)$.

121. $x^2 = (x^2 - y)\ln Cx$; $y = x^2$.　　**122.** $x = -y^2\ln Cx$; $y = 0$.

123. $x^2 y^4 \ln Cx^2 = 1$; $\; y = 0$.　　**124.** $y^2 e^{-\frac{1}{xy}} = C$; $\; y = 0$; $\; x = 0$.
125. $(2\sqrt{y} - x)\ln C(2\sqrt{y} - x) = x$; $2\sqrt{y} = x$.　　**126.** $1 - xy =$

$= Cx^3(2 + xy)$; $xy = -2$. **127.** $2\sqrt{\dfrac{1}{xy^2} - 1} = -\ln Cx$; $xy^2 = 1$.

128. $\arcsin\dfrac{y^2}{|x^3|} = \ln Cx^3$; $|x^3| = y^2$.　　**129.** $x^2 y \ln Cy = 1$; $y = 0$.
130. a) $y^2 = C(x+y)$; $y = -x$; b) $(y+x)^2(y-2x)^4 = C(y-x)^3$;

$y = x$. **131.** $y = C(x^2 + y^2)$. **132.** $x^2 + y^2 = Cx$. **133.** for $\dfrac{1}{\beta} - \dfrac{1}{\alpha} = 1$.

135. $f(t) \neq t$, $f(+\infty) = f(-\infty) \neq \infty$, $\displaystyle\int_{-\infty}^{+\infty} \dfrac{(tf(t)+1)\,dt}{(f(t)-t)(t^2+1)} = 0$.

5. Linear First Order Equations.

136. $y = Cx^2 + x^4$.　　**137.** $y = (2x+1)(C + \ln|2x+1|) + 1$.
138. $y = \sin x + C\cos x$. **139.** $y = e^x(\ln|x| + C)$. **140.** $xy = C - \ln|x|$.
141. $y = x(C + \sin x)$. **142.** $y = Ce^{x^2} - x^2 - 1$.　**143.** $y = C\ln^2 x - \ln x$.
144. $xy = (x^3 + C)^{-x}$. **145.** $x = y^2 + Cy$; $y = 0$. **146.** $x = e^y + Ce^{-y}$.
147. $x = (C - \cos y)\sin y$.　　**148.** $x = 2\ln y - y + 1 + Cy^2$; $y = 0$.
149. $x = Cy^3 + y^2$; $y = 0$. **150.** $(y-1)^2 x = y - \ln Cy$; $y = 0$.
151. $y(e^x + Ce^{2x}) = 1$; $y = 0$.　　**152.** $y(x+1)(\ln|x+1| + C) = 1$;
$y = 0$. **153.** $y^{-3} = C\cos^3 x - 3\sin x \cos^2 x$; $y = 0$. **154.** $y^3 = Cx^3 - 3x^2$.
155. $y^2 = Cx^2 - 2x$; $x = 0$.　　　**156.** $y = x^4 \ln^2 Cx$; $y = 0$.
157. $y^{-2} = x^4(2e^x + C)$; $y = 0$. **158.** $y^2 = x^2 - 1 + C\sqrt{|x^2 - 1|}$.
159. $x^2(C - \cos y) = y$; $y = 0$.　　　**160.** $xy(C - \ln^2 y) = 1$.
161. $x^2 = Ce^{2y} + 2y$. **162.** $y^2 = C(x+1)^2 - 2(x+1)$. **163.** $e^{-y} = Cx^2 + x$.
164. $\cos y = (x^2 - 1)\ln C(x^2 - 1)$. **165.** $y = 2e^x - 1$. **166.** $y = -2e^x$.

167. $y = \dfrac{2}{x} + \dfrac{4}{Cx^5 - x}$; $y = \dfrac{2}{x}$. **168.** $y = \dfrac{1}{x} + \dfrac{1}{Cx^{\frac{2}{3}} + x}$; $y = \dfrac{1}{x}$.

169. $y = x + \dfrac{x}{x+C}$; $y = x$. **170.** $y = x + 2 + \dfrac{4}{Ce^{4x} - 1}$; $y = x + 2$.

171. $y = e^x - \dfrac{1}{x+C}$; $y = e^x$.　　　**172.** $3x = C\sqrt{|y|} - y^2$; $y = 0$

173. $xy = Cx^3 + 2a^2$. 74. $xy = a^2 + Cy^2$. 175. In 20 min., 3.68

kg. 176. In 62 days. 177. In 24 days; in 23 years.

178. $y = \operatorname{tg} x - \sec x$. 179. $x(t) = \int\limits_{-\infty}^{t} e^{s-t} f(s)\, ds; \quad |x(t)| \leqslant M$.

182. $\dfrac{b}{a}$. 183. $\dfrac{b}{a}$. 184. $y(x) = -\int\limits_{0}^{\infty} \sin(x+s)\, e^{-\frac{s}{2}-\frac{1}{2}\sin s \cdot \cos(s+2x)}\, ds$.

185. $y(x) = x \int\limits_{+\infty}^{x} e^{x^2-t^2}\, dt \to -\dfrac{1}{2}$ for $x \to +\infty$.

6. Exact Equations.

186. $3x^2 y - y^3 = C$. 187. $x^2 - 3x^3 y^2 + y^4 = C$. 188. $xe^{-y} - y^2 = C$.

189. $4y \ln x + y^4 = C$. 190. $x + \dfrac{x^3}{y^2} + \dfrac{5}{y} = C$. 191. $x^2 + \dfrac{2}{3}(x^2-y)^{\frac{3}{2}} = C$.

192. $x - y^2 \cos^2 x = C$. 193. $x^3 + x^3 \ln y - y^2 = C$. 194. $x^2 + 1 = 2(C-2x) \sin y$. 195. $2x + \ln(x^2+y^2) = C$. 196. $x + \operatorname{arctg} \dfrac{x}{y} = C$.

197. $\sqrt{1+x^2} = xy + C$. 198. $2x^3 y^3 - 3x^2 = C$. 199. $y^2 = x^2(C-2y)$; $x = 0$. 200. $(x^2 - C)\, y = 2x$. 201. $x^2 + \ln y = Cx^3$; $x = 0$.

202. $y \sin xy = C$. 203. $\dfrac{x^2}{2} + xy + \ln|y| = C$; $y = 0$. 204. $-x + 1 = xy(\operatorname{arctg} y + C)$; $x = 0$; $y = 0$. 205. $x + 2\ln|x| + \dfrac{3}{2} y^2 - \dfrac{y}{x} = C$;

$x = 0$. 206. $\sin \dfrac{y}{x} = Ce^{-x^2}$. 207. $\ln|y| - ye^{-x} = C$; $y = 0$.

208. $\ln\left(\dfrac{x^2}{y^2} + 1\right) = 2y + C$; $y = 0$. 209. $x^2 y \ln Cxy = -1$; $x = 0$;

$y = 0$. 210. $x^2 + y^2 = y + Cx$; $x = 0$. 211. $x^2 y + \ln\left|\dfrac{x}{y}\right| = C$;

$x = 0$; $y = 0$. 212. $2xy^2 + \dfrac{1}{xy} = C$; $x = 0$; $y = 0$.

213. $\ln \dfrac{x+y}{y} + \dfrac{y(1+x)}{x+y} = C$; $y = 0$. 214. $\sin^2 y = Cx - x^2$;

$x = 0$. 215. $y = C \ln x^2 y$. 216. $\sin y = -(x^2+1) \ln C(x^2+1)$

217. $xy(C - x^2 - y^2) = 1$; $x = 0$; $y = 0$. 218. $y^2 = Cx^2 e^{x^2 y^2}$.

219. $x\sqrt{1 + \dfrac{y^2}{x^2}} + \ln\left(\dfrac{y}{x} + \sqrt{1 + \dfrac{y^2}{x^2}}\right) = C$; $x = 0$. 220. $x^3 - 4y^2 = Cy\sqrt[3]{xy}$; $x = 0$; $y = 0$.

8. Equations in which the Derivative Appears Implicitly.

241. $y = Ce^{\pm x}$. **242.** $y^2 = (x + C)^3$; $y = 0$. **243.** $y + x = (x + C)^3$;
$y = -x$. **244.** $(x + C)^2 + y^2 = 1$; $y = \pm 1$. **245.** $y(x + C)^2 = 1$; $y = 0$.
246. $y[1 + (x - C)^2] = 1$; $y = 0$; $y = 1$. **247.** $(y - x)^2 = 2C(x + y) - C^2$.

$y = 0$. **248.** $(x - 1)^{\frac{4}{3}} + y^{\frac{4}{3}} = C$. **249.** $4y = (x + C)^2$; $y = Ce^x$.
250. $y^2(1 - y) = (x + C)^2$; $y = 1$. **251.** $y = Ce^x$; $y = Ce^{-x} + x - 1$.
252. $x^2 y = C$; $y = Cx$. **253.** $x^2 + C^2 = 2Cy$; $y = \pm x$. **254.** $(x + C)^2 = 4Cy$;
$y = 0$; $y = x$. **255.** $\ln|1 \pm 2\sqrt{2y - x}| = 2(x + C \pm \sqrt{2y - x})$.

256. $4e^{-\frac{y}{3}} = (x + 2)^{\frac{4}{3}} + C$. **257.** $y = 2x^2 + C$; $y = -x^2 + C$.

258. $y = Cx^{-3} \pm 2\sqrt{x}$. **259.** $\ln Cy = x \pm 2e^{\frac{x}{2}}$, $\quad y = 0$.

260. $\ln Cy = x + \sin x$; $y = 0$. **261.** $\text{arctg } u + \frac{1}{2}\ln\left|\frac{u-1}{u+1}\right| = \pm x + C$,

where $u = \sqrt[4]{1 - \frac{1}{y^2}}$; $y = 0$; $y = \pm 1$. **262.** $x^2 + (Cy + 1)^2 = 1$; $y = 0$.
263. $(Cx + 1)^2 = 1 - y^2$; $y = \pm 1$. **264.** $2(x - C)^2 + 2y^2 = C^2$; $y = \pm x$.
265. $y = Ce^{\pm x} - x^2$. **266.** $y^2 = C^2 x - C$; $4xy^2 = -1$. **267.** $x = p^3 + p$,
$4y = 3p^4 + 2p^2 + C$. **268.** $x = \frac{2p}{p^2 - 1}$, $y = \frac{2}{p^2 - 1} - \ln|p^2 - 1| + C$.

269. $x = p\sqrt{p^2 + 1}$, $3y = (2p^2 - 1)\sqrt{p^2 + 1} + C$. **270.** $x = \ln p + \frac{1}{p}$;
$y = p - \ln p + C$. **271.** $x = 3p^2 + 2p + C$, $y = 2p^3 + p^2$; $y = 0$.
272. $x = 2\text{arctg } p + C$, $y = \ln(1 + p^2)$; $y = 0$. **273.** $x = \ln|p| \pm$
$\pm \frac{3}{2}\ln\left|\frac{\sqrt{p+1}-1}{\sqrt{p+1}+1}\right| \pm 3\sqrt{p+1} + C$, $y = p \pm (p+1)^{\frac{3}{2}}$, $y = \pm 1$.
274. $x = e^p + C$, $y = (p - 1)e^p$; $y = -1$.
275. $x = \pm\left(2\sqrt{p^2 - 1} + \arcsin\frac{1}{|p|}\right) + C$, $y = \pm p\sqrt{p^2 - 1}$; $y = 0$.

276. $x = \pm\left(\ln\left|\frac{1 - \sqrt{1-p}}{1 + \sqrt{1-p}}\right| + 3\sqrt{1-p}\right) + C$, $y = \pm p\sqrt{1-p}$;
$y = 0$. **277.** $x = \pm 2\sqrt{1 + p^2} - \ln(\sqrt{p^2 + 1} \pm 1) + C$,
$y = -p \pm p\sqrt{p^2 + 1}$; $y = 0$. **278.** $4y = C^2 - 2(x - C)^2$; $2y = x^2$.
279. $x = -\frac{p}{2} + C$, $5y = C^2 - \frac{5p^2}{4}$; $x^2 = 4y$. **280.** $\pm xp\sqrt{2\ln Cp} = 1$,
$y = \mp\left(\sqrt{2\ln Cp} - \frac{1}{\sqrt{2\ln Cp}}\right)$. **281.** $pxy = y^2 + p^3$, $y^2(2p + C) = p^4$;
$y = 0$. **282.** $y^2 = 2Cx - C\ln C$; $2x = 1 + 2\ln|y|$. **283.** $Cx = \ln Cy$;
$y = ex$. **284.** $xp^2 = C\sqrt{|p|} - 1$, $y = xp - x^2p^3$; $y = 0$.
285. $2p^2x = C - C^2p^2$, $py = C$; $32x^3 = -27y^4$. **286.** $y^2 = 2C^3x + C^2$;
$27x^2y^2 = 1$. **287.** $y = Cx - C^2$; $4y = x^2$. **288.** $x\sqrt{p} = \ln p + C$,
$y = \sqrt{p}(4 - \ln p - C)$; $y = 0$. **289.** $x = 3p^2 + C|p|^{-\frac{3}{2}}$,
$y = 2p^3 + 3C|p|^{-\frac{1}{2}}\text{sgn } p$; $y = 0$. **290.** $y = Cx - C - 2$. **291.** $x = Cp$,
$2y = C(p^2 + 1)$; $y = \pm x$. **292.** $x = C(p - 1)^{-2} + 2p + 1$,
$y = Cp^2(p-1)^{-2} + p^2$; $y = 0$; $y = x - 2$. **293.** $y = Cx - \ln C$;
$y = \ln x + 1$. **294.** $y = 2\sqrt{Cx} + C$; $y = -x$. **295.** $2C^2(y - Cx) = 1$;
$8y^3 = 27x^2$. **296.** $xp^2 = p + C$, $y = 2 + 2Cp^{-1} - \ln p$.
297. $C^3 = 3(Cx - y)$; $9y^2 = 4x^3$. **298.** $xy = a^2$. **299.** $x^2 + y^2 = 1$.
300. $x = \frac{p(p^2 + 2)}{\sqrt{p^2 + 1}^3}$, $y = \frac{p^2}{\sqrt{p^2 + 1}^3}$; $x = \frac{p}{\sqrt{p^2 + 1}^3}$, $y = \frac{2p^2 + 1}{\sqrt{p^2 + 1}^3}$.

9. Miscellaneous First Order Equations.

301. $y = x(Ce^{-x} - 1)$.   **302.** $(Cx + 1)y = (Cx - 1)$; $y = 1$.
303. $y(x^2 - C) = x$; $y = 0$.   **304.** $x(C - y) = C^2$; $x = 4y$.
305. $y(x + C) = x + 1$; $y = 0$. **306.** $x = Cy + y^3$; $y = 0$. **307.** $y = C$;
$y = C \pm e^x$. **308.** $y \ln Cx = -x$; $y = 0$. **309.** $y^2 = C(x^2 - 1)$; $x = \pm 1$.
310. $2y = 2C(x - 1) + C^2$; $2y = -(x-1)^2$.   **311.** $x = Cy + \ln^2 y$.

312. $y = Cx^2 e^{-\frac{3}{x}}$.   **313.** $(x - C)^2 + y^2 = C$; $4(y^2 - x) = 1$.
314. $4x^2 y = (x + 2C)^2$; $y = 0$.   **315.** $x = Ce^y + y^2 + 2y + 2$.
316. $3y = 3C(x - 2) + C^3$; $9y^2 = 4(2 - x)^3$.   **317.** $y^2 = C(xy - 1)$;
$xy = 1$. **318.** $4(x - C)^3 = 27(y - C)^2$; $y = x - 1$. **319.** $x + y = \text{tg}(y - C)$.
320. $x^3 y^2 + 7x = C$. **321.** $y(xy - 1) = Cx$. **322.** $-e^{-y} = \ln C(x - 2)$.

323. $x = y^2(C - 2\ln|y|)$; $y = 0$.   **324.** $3xy = C \pm 4x^{\frac{3}{2}}$.
325. $y^2(Ce^{x^2} + 1) = 1$; $y = 0$.   **326.** $y^2 = 2x \ln Cy$; $y = 0$.
327. $\ln(x^2 + y^2) + \text{arctg}\dfrac{y}{x} = C$.   **328.** $(x - 1)^2 y = x - \ln|x| + C$.
329. $C^2 x^2 + 2y^2 = 2C$; $2x^2 y^2 = 1$. **330.** $y(C\sqrt{|x^2 - 1|} - 2) = 1$; $y = 0$.
331. $y^2(Ce^{2x} + x + 0{,}5) = 1$; $y = 0$. **332.** $y^2 = 1 + C(x + 1)^2 e^{-2x}$;
$x = -1$.   **333.** $y \sin x - \dfrac{x^3}{3} + \dfrac{y^2}{2} = C$.   **334.** $x = 3p^2 + p^{-1}$,
$y = 2p^3 - \ln|p| + C$.   **335.** $3y^2 = 2\sin x + C\sin^{-2} x$.
336. $x(e^y + xy) = C$. **337.** $x(p - 1)^2 = \ln Cp$, $y = xp^2 + p$; $y = 0$;
$y = x + 1$.   **338.** $(x + 1)y = x^2 + x \ln Cx$. **339.** $y^2 + \sqrt{x^4 + y^4} = C$.
340. $px = C\sqrt{p} - 1$, $y = \ln p - C\sqrt{p} + 1$. **341.** $y = x \, \text{tg} \ln Cx$; $x = 0$.
342. $y^{\frac{2}{3}} = Ce^{2x} + \dfrac{x}{3} + \dfrac{1}{6}$; $y = 0$.   **343.** $x = Ce^{\sin y} - 2(1 + \sin y)$.

344. $Cy = C^2 e^x + 1$; $y = \pm 2e^{\frac{x}{2}}$.   **345.** $y^2 = (x^2 + C)e^{2x}$.

346. $y = Cx - \sqrt[3]{C^3 - 1}$; $y^{\frac{3}{2}} = x^{\frac{3}{2}} - 1$. **347.** $x(y^2 - 1)^2 = y^3 - 3y + C$;
$y = \pm 1$. **348.** $\sqrt{y - x} - \sqrt{x} = C$; $y = x$. **349.** $x\sqrt{y} = \sin x + C$;
$y = 0$.   **350.** $x = 4p^3 - \ln Cp$, $y = 3p^4 - p$; $y = 0$.
351. $y^2 + 2x^2 \ln Cy = 0$; $y = 0$.   **352.** $4x + y - 3 = 2\,\text{tg}\,(2x + C)$.
353. $xy \cos x - y^2 = C$. **354.** $4Cxy = C^2 x^4 - 1$. **355.** $xy(\ln^2 x + C) = 1$.
356. $2\sqrt{y - x^2} = x \ln Cx$; $y = x^2$. **357.** $\dfrac{y^2}{2} - \dfrac{1}{x} - xy = C$; $x = 0$.
358. $x = Cy^2 - y^2(y + 1)e^{-y}$; $y = 0$.   **359.** $y(\ln y - \ln x - 1) = C$.
360. $x = 2p - \ln p$, $y = p^2 - p + C$. **361.** $2x^5 - x^2 y^2 + y^3 + x = C$.
362. $(y - 4x + 2)^4 (2y + 2x - 1) = C$.   **363** $y^3 = (C - x^3)\sin^3 x$.
364. $p^2 x = p \sin p + \cos p + C$, $py = p \sin p + 2\cos p + 2C$; $y = 0$.
365. $x^2 y^2 - 1 = xy \ln Cy^2$; $y = 0$.   **366.** $y = C \cos x + \sin x$.
367. $|x| = \ln\left(\dfrac{y}{x} + \sqrt{1 + \dfrac{y^2}{x^2}}\right) + C$; $x = 0$.   **368.** $(y - x)^2 =$
$= 2C(x + y) - C^2$; $y^{\frac{2}{3}} - x^{\frac{2}{3}} = C$; $y = 0$. **369.** $27(y - 2x)^2 = (C - 2x)^3$;

$y = 2x$. **370.** $\sin \dfrac{y}{x} = -\ln Cx$. **371.** $x^2 (x^2y + \sqrt{1 + x^4y^2}) = C$.

372. $3\sqrt{y} = x^2 - 1 + C\sqrt[4]{|x^2 - 1|}$; $y = 0$. **373.** $x = \dfrac{C}{p^2} - p - \dfrac{3}{2}$,

$y = C\left(\dfrac{2}{p} - 1\right) - \dfrac{p^2}{2}$; $y = x+2$; $y = 0$. **374.** $(2x+3y-7)^3 = Ce^{x+2y}$.

375. $(x^2 + y + \ln Cy) y = x$; $y = 0$. **376.** $x = 2\sqrt{p^2 + 1} -$

$-\ln(1+\sqrt{p^2+1}) + \ln Cp$, $y = p\sqrt{p^2+1}$; $y = 0$. **377.** $y^2 = C\ln^2 x + 2\ln x$.

378. $x = Cue^u$, $4y = C^2e^{2u}(2u^2+2u+1)$; $x^2 = 2y$. **379.** $xy^2 \ln Cxy = 1$;

$x = 0$; $y = 0$. **380.** $x^2 \sin^2 y = 2\sin^3 y + C$. **381.** $1 - xy = (Cx - 1)^2$;

$xy = 1$. **382.** $xe^y = e^x + C$. **383.** $\sin(y-2x) - 2\cos(y-2x) = Ce^{x+2y}$.

384. $y = (2x + C)\sqrt{x^2 + 1} - x^2 - Cx - 2$. **385.** $(y + x^2)^2 (2y - x^2) = C$.

386. $(x-1)^2 = y^2(2x - 2\ln Cx)$; $y=0$. **387.** $x = p[\ln(1+\sqrt{p^2+1}) - \ln Cp]$,

$2y = xp - \sqrt{p^2 + 1}$; $2y = -1$. **388.** $(y + 3x + 7)(y - x - 1)^3 = C$.

389. $\sin y = Ce^{-x} + x - 1$. **390.** $y = C^2 (x - C)^2$; $16y = x^4$.

391. $y^2 = x - (x + 1)\ln C(x + 1)$. **392.** $e^y = x^2 \ln Cx$.

393. $(y - 2x\sqrt{y - x^2})(2\sqrt{y - x^2} + x) = C$. **394.** $xy^2 = \ln x^2 - \ln Cy$;

$x = 0$, $y = 0$. **395.** $x(y^2 + x^2) = \dfrac{2}{5} y^5 + \dfrac{4}{3} x^2y^3 + 2x^4y + Cx^5$;

$x = 0$. **396.** $(u - 1)\ln Cx^6 (u - 1)^5 (u + 2)^4 = 3$, with $u^3 = \dfrac{y^2}{x^2} - 2$;

$y^2 = 3x^2$. **397.** $\sqrt{y} = (x^2 - 1)(2\ln|x^2 - 1| + C)$; $y = 0$.

398. $x^2 - (x - 1)\ln(y + 1) - y = C$. **399.** $\operatorname{tg} y = x^2 + Cx$;

$y = (2k + 1)\cdot\dfrac{\pi}{2}$, $k = 0, \pm 1, \pm 2, \ldots$ **400.** $y^2 = Cx^2 + C^2$.

401. $x^3 = Ce^y - y - 2$. **402.** $y + 1 = x\ln C(y + 1)$; $y = -1$.

403. $y^2 = 2C^2(x - C)$; $8x^3 = 27y^2$. **404.** $x^6 = y^3(C - y\ln y + y)$;

$y = 0$. **405.** $\ln C(u - v)^3\left(u^2 + uv + \dfrac{v^2}{3}\right)^2 = 2\arctan\dfrac{2u + v}{v}$, where $u^3 = y$

$v^2 = x$; $y^2 = x^3$. **406.** $(y - 1)^2 = x^2 + Cx$. **407.** $(x^2 + y^2)(Cx + 1) = x$.

408. $3x + y^3 - 1 = \operatorname{tg}(3x + C)$. **409.** $(C - x^2)\sqrt{y^2 + 1} = 2x$.

410. $(x^2 + y^2 + 1)^2 = 4x^2 + C$. **411.** $xy - x = y(y - x)\ln\left|\dfrac{Cy}{y - x}\right|$;

$x = 0$; $y = 0$; $y = x$. **412.** $y = \pm x \operatorname{ch}(x + C)$; $y = \pm x$.

413. $\sqrt{y^2 + 1} = x(Ce^x - 1)$. **414.** $(y - x)\ln C\dfrac{x - 1}{x + 1} = 2$; $y = x$.

415. $(Ce^{x^2} + 2x^2 + 2)\cos y = 1$. **416.** $(y^2 - Cx + 1)^2 = 4(1 - C) y^2$;

$y = \pm x$. **417.** $y^2 + xy - 1 = Ce^{\frac{x^2}{2}}$. **418.** $6x^3y^4 + 2x^3y^3 + 3x^2y^4 = C$.

419. $x + \dfrac{1}{x} + y^2 - 2y + 2 = Ce^{-y}$; $x = 0$. **420.** $e^y(C^2x^2 + 1) = 2C$,

$x^2 = e^{-2y}$.

10. Equations which can be Reduced to Equations of Lower Order.

421. $C_1 x - C_1^2 y = \ln|C_1 x + 1| + C_2$; $\quad 2y = x^2 + C$; $\quad y = C$.

422. $9C_1^2 (y - C_2)^2 = 4(C_1 x + 1)^3$; $\quad y = \pm x + C$. $\quad$ **423.** $C_1 y^2 - 1 = (C_1 x + C_2)^2$. **424.** $y^3 = C_1 (x + C_2)^2$; $\quad y = C$. **425.** $y = C_1 \operatorname{tg}(C_1 x + C_2)$;

$\ln\left|\dfrac{y - C_1}{y + C_1}\right| = 2C_1 x + C_2$; $y(C - x) = 1$; $\quad y = C$. **426.** $C_1 y = \pm \sin(C_1 x + C_2)$;

$C_1 y = \pm \operatorname{sh}(C_1 x + C_2)$; $\quad y = C \pm x$. $\quad$ **427.** $y = C_1 (x - e^{-x}) + C_2$.

428. $\quad y = C_3 - (x + C_1) \ln C_2 (x + C_1)$; $\qquad y = C_1 x + C_2$.

429. $y + C_1 \ln|y| = x + C_2$; $\quad y = C$. **430.** $2y = C_1 \cos 2x + x^2 + C_2 x + C_3$.

431. $y = C_1 [1 \pm \operatorname{ch}(x + C_2)]$. $\qquad$ **432.** $x = C_1 p + 3p^2$; $\quad y = \dfrac{12}{5} p^5 +$

$+ \dfrac{5}{4} C_1 p^4 + C_1^2 \dfrac{p^3}{6} + C_2$; $\quad y = C$. $\qquad$ **433.** $y = C_1 \dfrac{x^2}{2} - C_1^2 x + C_2$;

$y = \dfrac{x^3}{12} + C$. $\qquad$ **434.** $e^y + C_1 = (x + C_2)^2$. $\qquad$ **435.** $2y = C_1 x^2 -$

$- 2C_1^2 (x + C_1) \ln(x + C_1) + C_2 x + C_3$; $\qquad 6y = x^3 + C_1 x + C_2$.

436. $y = \operatorname{ch}(x + C_1) + C_2$. $\qquad$ **437.** $e^y \sin^2(C_1 x + C_2) = 2C_1^2$;

$e^y \operatorname{sh}^2(C_1 x + C_2) = 2C_1^2$; $e^y (x + C)^2 = 2$. $\quad$ **438.** $y = C_1 \dfrac{x^3}{6} - C_1^3 \dfrac{x^2}{2} +$

$+ C_2 x + C_3$; $y = \dfrac{8}{315} x^3 \sqrt[3]{3x} + C_1 x + C_2$. **439.** $3C_1 y = (x - C_1)^3 + C_2$;

$y = C$; $y = C - 2x^2$. **440.** $\ln\left|y^2 + C_1 \pm \sqrt{y^4 + 2C_1 y^2 + 1}\right| = 2x + C_2$;

$y = \pm 1$. $\qquad$ **441.** $x = 3C_1 p^2 + \ln C_2 p$, $\qquad y = 2C_1 p^3 + p$; $\qquad y = C$.

442. $x = C_1 e^p - 2p - 2$, $y = C_1 (p - 1) e^p - p^2 + C_2$. **443.** $12(C_1 y - x) = C_1^2 (x + C_2)^3 + C_3$. **444.** $y = C_1 (x \sqrt{x^2 - 1} - \ln|x + \sqrt{x^2 - 1}|) +$

$+ x^2 + C_2$. **445.** $\ln y = C_1 \operatorname{tg}(C_1 x + C_2)$; $\ln\left|\dfrac{\ln y - C_1}{\ln y + C_1}\right| = 2C_1 x + C_2$;

$(C - x) \ln y = 1$; $\quad y = C$. $\qquad$ **446.** $x = u - \ln|1 + u| + C_2$, where

$u = \pm \sqrt{1 + 4C_1 y}$; $y = C$; $y = Ce^{-x}$. **447.** $C_1^2 y = (C_1^2 x^2 + 1) \operatorname{arctg} C_1 x -$

$- C_1 x + C_2$; $2y = k\pi x^2 + C$, $k = 0, \pm 1, \pm 2, \ldots$ **448.** $x = \ln|p| +$

$+ 2C_1 p - C_2$, $\qquad y = p + C_1 p^2 + C_3$; $\qquad y = C_1 x + C_2$.

449. $C_1^2 y + 1 = \pm \operatorname{ch}(C_1 x + C_2)$; $\qquad C_1^2 y - 1 = \sin(C_1 x + C_2)$;

$2y = (x + C)^2$; $\quad y = 0$. $\qquad$ **450.** $y = C_2 - \ln\left|\cos\left(\dfrac{x^2}{2} + C_1\right)\right|$.

451. $6y = x^3 \ln|x| + C_1 x^3 + C_2 x^2 + C_3 x + C_4$.

452. $y = x \displaystyle\int_0^x \dfrac{\sin t}{t} \, dt + \cos x + C_1 x + C_2$.

453. $y = C_1 \left[x \displaystyle\int_0^x e^{t^2} \, dt - \dfrac{1}{2} (e^{x^2} - 1) \right] + C_2 x + C_3$.

454. $y = \dfrac{x^2}{2} \displaystyle\int_1^x \dfrac{e^t}{t}\, dt - \dfrac{x+1}{2} e^x + C_1 x^2 \ln|x| + C_2 x^2 + C_3 x + C_4.$

455. $y = C_2 e^{C_1 x} + C_3 e^{-C_1 x};\quad y = C_2 \cos C_1 x + C_3 \sin C_1 x;\quad y = C_1 x + C_2.$

456. $C_1 y = \ln|C_1 x + C_2| + C_3;\quad y = C_1 x + C_2.$ **457.** $C_1 y - 1 = C_2 e^{C_1 x};$
$y = C - x;\qquad y = 0.$ **458.** $y = \pm \sqrt{C_1 x + C_2} + C_3 x + C_4;$
$y = C_1 x^2 + C_2 x + C_3.$ **459.** $y^2 = x^2 + C_1 x + C_2.$

460. $y = e^{\frac{x^2}{2}}\left(C_1 \displaystyle\int e^{-\frac{x^2}{2}}\, dx + C_2 \right) - 1.$ **461.** $y = C_1 \operatorname{tg}(C_1 \ln C_2 x);$
$C_2(y + C_1)\,|x|^{2C_1} = y - C_1;\quad y \ln Cx = -1.$ **462.** $y = 4C_1 \operatorname{tg}(C_1 x^2 + C_2);$
$2\ln\left|\dfrac{y - C_1}{y + C_1}\right| = C_1 x^2 + C_2;\quad y(C - x^2) = 4;\quad y = C.$ **463.** $y = C_2 e^{Cx^3}.$

464. $\ln C_2 y = 4x^{\frac{5}{2}} + C_1 x.$ **465.** $y = C_2 (x + \sqrt{x^2 + 1})^{C_1}.$

466. $y^2 = C_1 x^3 + C_2.$ **467.** $y = C_2 x e^{-\frac{C_1}{x}}.$ **468.** $y = C_2\,|x|^{C_1 - \frac{1}{2}\ln|x|}.$

469. $y = C_2\left|\dfrac{x}{x + C_1}\right|^{\frac{1}{C_1}};\quad y = C.$ **470.** $|y|^{C_1^2 + 1} = C_2\left(x - \dfrac{1}{C_1}\right)|x + C_1|^{C_1^2};$
$y = C.$ **471.** $y = C_2 x (\ln C_1 x)^2;\quad y = Cx.$ **472.** $\ln|y| = \ln|x^2 - 2x + C_1| +$
$+ \displaystyle\int \dfrac{2dx}{(x-1)^2 + C_1 - 1} + C_2;\quad y = C.$ **473.** $4C_1 y^2 = 4x + x\,(C_1 \ln C_2 x)^2.$

474. $y = -x \ln(C_2 \ln C_1 x);\quad y = Cx.$ **475.** $\dfrac{y}{x} = C_2 - 3\ln\left|\dfrac{1}{x} - C_1\right|;$
$y = Cx.$ **476.** $x^2 y = C_1 \operatorname{tg}(C_1 \ln C_2 x);\quad C_2(x^2 y + C_1)\,|x|^{2C_1} = x^2 y - C_1;$
$x^2 y \ln Cx = -1.$ **477.** $4(C_1 y - 1) = C_1^2 \ln^2 C_2 x.$ **478.** $Cy = x^{\frac{3}{2}}(C_2 x^C + 2);$
$y = Cx^{\frac{5}{2}}.$ **479.** $2C_2 x^2 y = (C_2 x - C_1)^2 - 1;\qquad xy = \pm 1.$
480. $2C_1 C_2 y = C_2^2\,|x|^{2 + C_1} + |x|^{2 - C_1}.$ **501.** $(3 - x) y^5 = 8\,(x + 2).$

502. $y(x + 2) = -x - 6.$ **503.** $(1 - \ln x)^2\, y = x^2.$ **504.** $y = 3\operatorname{th}^2 \dfrac{x\sqrt{3}}{2} - 2.$

505. $\ln\operatorname{tg}\left(\dfrac{y}{2} + \dfrac{\pi}{6}\right) = 2x + 2.$ **506.** a) $4(C_1 y - 1) = C_1^2 (x + C_2)^2;$

b) $y\sqrt{\dfrac{C_1}{y} - 1} + C_1 \arccos \sqrt{\dfrac{y}{C_1}} = C_2 \pm x.$ **507.** $y = C_2 -$
$- k \ln\cos\left(\dfrac{x}{k} + C_1\right).$ **508.** $y = \dfrac{p}{2T}\,x^2 + C_1 x + C_2.$

509. $ay = \cosh(ax + C_1) + C_2,$ where $a = q/T.$

11. Linear Equations with Constant Coefficients.

511. $y = C_1 e^x + C_2 e^{-2x}$. **512.** $y = C_1 e^{-x} + C_2 e^{-3x}$. **513.** $y = C_1 + C_2 e^{2x}$.

514. $y = C_1 e^{2x} + C_2 e^{\frac{x}{2}}$. **515.** $y = e^{2x}(C_1 \cos x + C_2 \sin x)$.

516. $y = e^{-x}(C_1 \cos 3x + C_2 \sin 3x)$. **517.** $y = C_1 \cos 2x + C_2 \sin 2x$.

518. $y = C_1 e^{2x} + e^{-x}(C_2 \cos x \sqrt{3} + C_3 \sin x \sqrt{3})$. **519.** $y = C_1 e^x +$
$+ C_2 e^{-x} + C_3 \cos x + C_4 \sin x$. **520.** $y = e^x(C_1 \cos x + C_2 \sin x) +$
$+ e^{-x}(C_3 \cos x + C_4 \sin x)$. **521.** $y = e^{\sqrt{3}\,x}(C_1 \cos x + C_2 \sin x) +$
$+ C_3 \cos 2x + C_4 \sin 2x + e^{-\sqrt{3}x}(C_5 \cos x + C_6 \sin x)$.

522. $y = e^x(C_1 + C_2 x)$. **523.** $y = e^{-\frac{x}{2}}(C_1 + C_2 x)$. **524.** $y = C_1 + C_2 x +$
$+ C_3 x^2 + e^{3x}(C_4 + C_5 x)$. **525.** $y = C_1 + C_2 e^x + C_3 e^{-x} + C_4 e^{3x} + C_5 e^{-3x}$
526. $y = (C_1 + C_2 x) \cos x + (C_3 + C_4 x) \sin x$. **527.** $y = e^x(C_1 + C_2 x + C_3 x^2)$.
528. $y = e^x(C_1 + C_2 x) + C_3 e^{-x}$. **529.** $y = C_1 e^x + C_2 e^{-x} + C_3 e^{2x} + C_4 e^{-2x}$.
530. $y = C_1 + (C_2 + C_3 x) \cos 2x + (C_4 + C_5 x) \sin 2x$.
531. $y = e^x(C_1 + C_2 x) + C_3 e^{-2x}$. **532.** $y = C_1 \cos x + C_2 \sin x +$
$+ C_3 \cos x \sqrt{3} + C_4 \sin x \sqrt{3}$. **533.** $y = C_1 e^{-x} + C_2 e^{3x} + \frac{1}{5} e^{4x}$.
534. $y = C_1 \cos x + C_2 \sin x + (2x - 2) e^x$. **535.** $y = C_1 e^x + C_2 e^{-x} +$
$+ xe^x + x^2 + 2$. **536.** $y = C_1 e^x + C_2 e^{-2x} + \left(\frac{x^2}{2} - \frac{x}{3}\right) e^x$.
537. $y = C_1 e^x + C_2 e^{2x} + 0.1 \sin x + 0.3 \cos x$. **538.** $y = C_1 \cos x +$
$+ C_2 \sin x - 2x \cos x$. **539.** $y = C_1 e^x + C_2 e^{4x} - (2x^2 - 2x + 3) e^{2x}$.
540. $y = C_1 e^x + C_2 e^{2x} + (0.1x - 0.12) \cos x - (0.3x + 0.34) \sin x$.
541. $y = C_1 e^x + C_2 e^{-4x} - \frac{x}{5} e^{-4x} - \left(\frac{x}{6} + \frac{1}{36}\right) e^{-x}$. **542.** $y = C_1 e^x +$
$+ C_2 e^{-3x} + \left(\frac{x^3}{12} - \frac{x^2}{16} + \frac{x}{32}\right) e^x$. **543.** $y = e^{2x}(C_1 \cos 2x + C_2 \sin 2x) +$
$+ 0.25 e^{2x} + 0.1 \cos 2x + 0.05 \sin 2x$. **544.** $y = C_1 e^{3x} + C_2 e^{-3x} +$
$+ e^{3x}\left(\frac{6}{37} \sin x - \frac{1}{37} \cos x\right)$. **545.** $y = (C_1 + C_2 x + x^3) e^x$.
546. $y = \left(C_1 - \frac{x^2}{4}\right) \cos x + \left(C_2 + \frac{x}{4}\right) \sin x$. **547.** $y = (C_1 + C_2 x) e^{-2x} +$
$+ \left(\frac{x}{16} - \frac{1}{32}\right) e^{2x}$. **548.** $y = C_1 + C_2 e^{5x} - 0.2x^3 - 0.12x^2 - 0.048x +$
$+ 0.02 (\cos 5x - \sin 5x)$. **575.** $y = e^x (x \ln|x| + C_1 x + C_2)$.
576. $y = (e^{-x} + e^{-2x}) \ln(e^x + 1) + C_1 e^{-x} + C_2 e^{-2x}$.
577. $y = (C_1 + \ln|\sin x|) \sin x + (C_2 - x) \cos x$. **578.** $y = \sin 2x \times$
$\times \ln|\cos x| - x \cos 2x + C_1 \sin 2x + C_2 \cos 2x$. **579.** $y = e^{-x} \times$
$\times \left(\frac{4}{5}(x + 1)^{\frac{5}{2}} + C_1 + C_2 x\right)$. **580.** $y = -\frac{1}{x} + C_1 e^x + C_2 e^{-x}$.
581. $y = 2 + e^{-x}$. **582.** $y = (7 - 3x) e^{x-2}$. **583.** $y = 2 \cos x - 5 \sin x + 2e^x$.
584. $y = e^{2x-1} - 2e^x + e - 1$. **585.** $y = \frac{\operatorname{sh} x}{\operatorname{sh} 1} - 2x$.
586. $y = 1 - \sin x - \cos x$. **587.** No solution. **588.** $y = 2x - \pi +$
$+ \pi \cos x + C \sin x$, C — arbitrary. **589.** $y = C_1 x^2 + C_2 x^3$.
590. $y = C_1 x^3 + C_2 x^{-1}$. **591.** $y = x^3 (C_1 + C_2 \ln|x| + C_3 \ln^2|x|)$.
592. $y = C_1 + C_2 \ln|x| + C_3 x^3$. **593.** $y = x (C_1 + C_2 \ln|x|) + 2x^3$.
594. $y = C_1 \cos(2 \ln|x|) + C_2 \sin(2 \ln|x|) + 2x$. **595.** $y = C_1 x^2 +$
$+ \frac{1}{x}\left(C_2 - \frac{2}{3} \ln x - \ln^2 x\right)$. **596.** $y = x^2 (C_1 \cos \ln|x| + C_2 \sin \ln|x| + 3)$.
597. $y = C_1 x^3 + C_2 x^{-2} + x^3 \ln|x| - 2x^2$. **598.** $y = C_1 x^2 + C_2 x^{-1} +$
$+ 0.1 \cos \ln x - 0.3 \sin \ln x$. **599.** $y = (x - 2)^2 (C_1 + C_2 \ln|x - 2|) +$
$+ x - 1.5$. **600.** $y = C_1 \left(x + \frac{3}{2}\right) + C_2 \left|x + \frac{3}{2}\right|^{\frac{3}{2}} + C_3 \left|x + \frac{3}{2}\right|^{\frac{1}{2}}$.

12. Linear Equations with Variable Coefficients.

601. No. 602. Yes. 603. No. 604. No. 605. Yes. 606. No.

607. Yes. 608. No. 609. No. 610. Yes. 611. No. 612. Yes.

613. Yes. 614. Yes. 615. No. 616. No. 617. Yes. 618. No.

619. Yes. 620. No. 621 Yes. 622. No.

624. $y'' - y' \operatorname{ctg} x = 0$. **625.** $(x-1) y'' - xy' + y = 0$.

626. $y''' - y'' = 0$. **627.** $(2x^2 + 6x - 9) y'' - (4x + 6) y' + 4y = 0$.

628. $y'' - y = 0$. **629.** $(x^2 - 2x + 2) y''' - x^2 y'' + 2xy' - 2y = 0$.

630. $x^2 y'' - 3xy' + 3y = 0$. **631.** $y = C_1 x + C_2 e^{-2x}$.

632. $y = C_1 \left(1 + \dfrac{1}{x}\right) + C_2 \left(\dfrac{x}{2} + 1 - \dfrac{x+1}{x} \ln |x + 1|\right)$.

633. $y = e^x (C_1 x^2 + C_2)$. **634.** $xy = C_1 e^{-x} + C_2 e^x$.

635. $y = C_1 \operatorname{tg} x + C_2 (1 + x \operatorname{tg} x)$. **636.** $y = C_1 (1 + x \ln |x|) + C_2 x$.

637. $y = C_1 (e^x - 1) + \dfrac{C_2}{e^x + 1}$. **638.** $y = C_1 x + C_2 (\ln x + 1)$.

639. $y = C_1 \sin x + C_2 \left(2 - \sin x \cdot \ln \dfrac{1 + \sin x}{1 - \sin x}\right)$.

640. $y = \dfrac{x}{(x^2 + 1)^{\frac{3}{2}}} \left[C_1 \left(\ln (x + \sqrt{x^2 + 1}) - \dfrac{\sqrt{x^2 + 1}}{x}\right) + C_2\right]$.

641. $y = C_1 e^{2x} + C_2 (3x + 1) e^{-x}$. **642.** $y = (C_1 + C_2 x) e^{-x^2}$.

643. $y = C_1 (2x + 1) + C_2 e^{2x}$. **644.** $y = C_1 (x + 1) + C_2 x^{-1}$.

645. $y = C_1 (x + 2) + C_2 x^2$. **646.** $y = C_1 (x^2 + 2) + C_2 x^3$.

647. $y = C_1 (x^2 + 1) + C_2 [x + (x^2 + 1) \operatorname{arctg} x]$.

648. $y = C_1 \sqrt{|x|} + C_2 (x - 2)$. **649.** $y = C_1 x + C_2 e^x + C_3 e^{-x}$.

650. $y = C_1 x + C_2 x^{-1} + C_3 (x \ln |x| + 1)$. **651.** $y = C_1 x + C_2 e^x + C_3 (x^2 - 1)$.

652. $y = C_1 (x + 2) + \dfrac{C_2}{x} + \left(\dfrac{x}{2} + 1\right) \ln |x| + \dfrac{3}{2}$.

653. $y = C_1 (2x - 1) + C_2 e^{-x} + \dfrac{x^2 + 1}{2}$. **654.** $y = \dfrac{C_1}{x+1} + \dfrac{C_2}{x-1} + x$.

655. $y = C_1 (x^2 + 1) + C_2 x^{-1} + 2x$. **656.** $z'' + z = 0$. **657.** $z'' - z = 0$.

658. $z'' = 0$. **659.** $x^2 z'' - 2z = 0$. **660.** $4x^2 z'' + (4x^2 + 1) z = 0$.

661. $y''_{tt} - y = 0$. **662.** $y''_{tt} + y = 0$. **663.** $(t^2 - 1) y''_{tt} - 2y = 0$.

664. $y''_{tt} + t^2 y = 0$. **665.** $8 y''_{tt} + t^2 y = 0$. **666.** $\dfrac{\pi}{\sqrt{m}}$;

The number of zeros lies between $\dfrac{(b - a) \sqrt{m}}{\pi} - 1$ (not inclusive)

and $\dfrac{(b - a) \sqrt{m}}{\pi} + 1$ (inclusive).

667. $0{,}33 < d < 0{,}5$. **668.** $15{,}7 < d < 32$.

669. $0{,}49 < d < 1$. **670.** $0{,}15 < d < 1{,}2$. **671.** $15 \leqslant N \leqslant 41$.

677. $u_{tt}^{''} + \left(\pm 1 + \psi^3 \psi_{xx}^{''} \right) u = 0, \quad t = \int \dfrac{dx}{(\psi(x))^2}, \quad y = \psi u$.

In problems 680, 681, 684, 685, 686, 688, 690, the second solution is obtained by replacing the cos function by the sin function.

680. $y_1 = \dfrac{1}{\sqrt{x}} \cos \dfrac{x^2}{2} + O\left(x^{-\frac{5}{2}} \right)$. **681.** $y_1 = e^{-\frac{x}{2}} \cos e^x + O\left(e^{-\frac{3}{2} x} \right)$.

682. $y_{1,2} = x^{\frac{1}{4}} e^{\pm 2\sqrt{x}} \left(1 + O\left(x^{-\frac{1}{2}} \right) \right)$. **683.** $y_{1,2} = x^{-\frac{1}{4}} e^{\pm \frac{2}{3} x^{\frac{3}{2}}} \times$

$\times \left(1 + O\left(x^{-\frac{3}{2}} \right) \right)$. **684.** $y_1 = x^{-\frac{3}{4}} \cos 2\sqrt{x} + O\left(x^{-\frac{5}{4}} \right)$.

685. $y_1 = e^{\frac{(x-1)^2}{2}} \left[(2x)^{-\frac{1}{4}} \cos \dfrac{(2x)^{\frac{3}{2}}}{3} + O\left(x^{-\frac{7}{4}} \right) \right]$.

686. $y_1 = \dfrac{1}{x} \cos \dfrac{x^3}{3} + O\left(\dfrac{1}{x^2} \right)$. **687.** $y_{1,2} = x^{\frac{1 \pm \sqrt{5}}{2}} (1 + O(x^{-2}))$.

688. $y_1 = \sqrt{\dfrac{x}{\ln x}} \left[\cos \left(\dfrac{1}{2} \ln^2 x - \dfrac{1}{8} \ln \ln x \right) + O(\ln^{-2} x) \right]$.

689. $y_{1,2} = \left[1 \pm \dfrac{3}{32x^2} + \dfrac{105}{2048x^4} + O(x^{-6}) \right] \dfrac{e^{\pm x^2}}{\sqrt{2x}}$.

690. $y_1 = x^{\frac{1}{4}} \left(1 + \dfrac{3}{64x} \right) \cos \left(2\sqrt{x} + \dfrac{3}{16\sqrt{x}} \right) + O\left(x^{-\frac{5}{4}} \right)$.

13. Series Development of Solutions of Equations.

691. $y = 1 + x + \dfrac{x^2}{2} + \dfrac{2x^3}{3} + \dfrac{7x^4}{12} + \dots$

692. $y = 1 + x + \dfrac{x^3}{3} - \dfrac{x^4}{3} + \dots$ **693** $y = \dfrac{x^2}{2} + \dfrac{x^3}{6} + \dfrac{x^4}{6} + \dots$

694. $y = x + x^2 - \dfrac{x^3}{6} - \dfrac{x^4}{4} - \dots$

695. $y = 1 + 2(x-1) + 4(x-1)^2 + \dfrac{25}{3}(x-1)^3 + \dfrac{81}{4}(x-1)^4 + \dots$

696. $y = 1 + 2x - \dfrac{x^2}{2} - \dfrac{x^3}{3} - \dfrac{x^4}{3} - \dots$ **697.** $y = 4 - 2x + 2x^2 -$

$- 2x^3 + \dfrac{19}{6} x^4 + \dots$ **698.** $R > 0{,}73$.

699. The error is less than 0.00 024.

700. $y_1 = 1 + \dfrac{x^4}{3 \cdot 4} + \dfrac{x^8}{3 \cdot 4 \cdot 7 \cdot 8} + \ldots, \; y_2 = x + \dfrac{x^5}{4 \cdot 5} + \dfrac{x^9}{4 \cdot 5 \cdot 8 \cdot 9} + \ldots$

701. $y_1 = 1 + \dfrac{x^2}{1} + \dfrac{x^4}{1 \cdot 3} + \dfrac{x^6}{1 \cdot 3 \cdot 5} + \ldots, \quad y_2 = x + \dfrac{x^3}{2} + \dfrac{x^5}{2 \cdot 4} +$

$+ \dfrac{x^7}{2 \cdot 4 \cdot 6} + \ldots = x e^{\frac{x^2}{2}}.$ **702.** $y_1 = 1 + x^2 + x^4 + \ldots = \dfrac{1}{1 - x^2},$

$y_2 = x + x^3 + x^5 + \ldots = \dfrac{x}{1 - x^2}.$ **703.** $y_1 = 1 - \dfrac{3}{2} x^2 +$

$+ \dfrac{3 \cdot 5}{2 \cdot 4} x^4 - \ldots = (1 + x^2)^{-\frac{3}{2}}, \qquad y_2 = x - \dfrac{4}{3} x^3 + \dfrac{4 \cdot 6}{3 \cdot 5} x^5 - \ldots$

704. $y_1 = 1 - \dfrac{x^2}{2} - \dfrac{x^3}{2} - \dfrac{11 x^4}{24} - \ldots, \; y_2 = x + x^2 + \dfrac{5 x^3}{6} + \dfrac{3 x^4}{4} + \ldots$

705. $y_1 = 1 + x - x^3 - x^4 + x^6 + x^7 - \ldots = \dfrac{1}{1 - x + x^2}, \; y_2 = xy_1.$

706. $y_1 = 1 - \dfrac{x^3}{6} - \dfrac{x^5}{40} + \ldots, \qquad y_2 = x + \dfrac{x^3}{6} - \dfrac{x^4}{12} + \ldots$

707. $y_1 = 1 - \dfrac{x^3}{6} + \dfrac{x^5}{120} + \ldots, \qquad y_2 = x - \dfrac{x^4}{12} + \dfrac{x^6}{180} + \ldots$

708. $y_1 = 1 + \dfrac{x^2}{2} + \dfrac{x^3}{12} + \dfrac{5 x^4}{72} + \ldots, \qquad y_2 = x + \dfrac{x^3}{6} + \dfrac{x^4}{24} + \ldots$

709. $y_1 = 1 - \dfrac{x^3}{6} + \ldots, \; y_2 = x + \dfrac{x^3}{3} - \dfrac{x^4}{12} + \ldots, \; y_3 = x^2 + \dfrac{x^4}{4} - \ldots$

710. $y_1 = 1 - \dfrac{x^2}{3!} + \dfrac{x^4}{5!} - \ldots = \dfrac{\sin x}{x}, \; y_2 = \dfrac{1}{x} - \dfrac{x}{2!} + \dfrac{x^3}{4!} - \ldots = \dfrac{\cos x}{x}.$

711. $y_1 = \dfrac{1}{x} + 1 + \dfrac{x}{2!} + \dfrac{x^2}{3!} + \ldots = \dfrac{e^x}{x}, \qquad y_2 = x^{\frac{1}{2}} \Big(1 + \dfrac{2x}{5} +$

$+ \dfrac{(2x)^2}{5 \cdot 7} + \dfrac{(2x)^3}{5 \cdot 7 \cdot 9} + \ldots \Big).$ **712.** $y_1 = x^{\frac{1}{3}} \Big(1 + \dfrac{x^2}{5 \cdot 6} + \dfrac{x^4}{5 \cdot 6 \cdot 11 \cdot 12} + \ldots \Big),$

$y_2 = x^{\frac{2}{3}} \Big(1 + \dfrac{x^2}{6 \cdot 7} + \dfrac{x^4}{6 \cdot 7 \cdot 12 \cdot 13} + \ldots \Big).$ **713.** $y_1 = \dfrac{1}{x} + 1 + \dfrac{x}{2},$

$y_2 = x^2 + \dfrac{x^3}{4} + \dfrac{x^4}{4 \cdot 5} + \dfrac{x^5}{4 \cdot 5 \cdot 6} + \ldots = 6 \Big(\dfrac{e^x - 1}{x} - 1 - \dfrac{x}{2} \Big).$

714. $y_1 = \dfrac{1}{x^2} - \dfrac{1}{x} + \dfrac{1}{2} + \dfrac{x^2}{8} + \dfrac{x^3}{40} + \dfrac{7 x^4}{720} + \ldots, \quad y_2 = x + \dfrac{x^2}{2} +$

$+ \dfrac{x^3}{5} + \dfrac{x^4}{20} + \ldots$ **715.** $y_1 = x + x^2 + \dfrac{x^3}{2!} + \dfrac{x^4}{3!} + \ldots = x e^x.$

716. $y_1 = 1 + \dfrac{x^2}{2^2} + \dfrac{x^4}{2^2 \cdot 4^2} + \dfrac{x^6}{2^2 \cdot 4^2 \cdot 6^2} + \ldots$ **717.** $y_2 = \Big(1 + \dfrac{x^2}{2^2} +$

$+ \dfrac{x^4}{2^2 \cdot 4^2} + \ldots \Big) \ln x - \dfrac{x^2}{4} - \dfrac{3 x^4}{128} - \ldots$

718. y_1, y_2 are power series in

the extended sense, with irrational exponents. **719.** y_1, y_2

are series with complex exponents. **720.** There is no solution

in series, even in the extended sense, since the radius of con-

vergence of the putative solution $y = 1 + 1! x + 2! x^2 + 3! x^3 + \ldots$ is 0.

721. $y = \dfrac{2}{\pi} + \dfrac{4}{\pi} \displaystyle\sum_{k=1}^{\infty} \dfrac{1}{16k^4 - 4k^2 + 1}\left(\cos 2kx - \dfrac{2k}{4k^2 - 1}\sin 2kx\right).$

722. $y = \displaystyle\sum_{k=1}^{\infty} \dfrac{(k^3 + k)\cos kx - \sin kx}{2^k\,[(k^3 + k)^2 + 1]}.$ **723.** $y = \dfrac{1}{z} + \mu\left(z^2 - \dfrac{1}{z^2}\right) +$

$+ \mu^2\left(-\dfrac{z^5}{7} + \dfrac{2z}{3} - \dfrac{32}{21z^2} + \dfrac{1}{z^3}\right) + \ldots, \quad z = x + 1.$

724. $y = 2\sqrt{x} + 2\mu\left(x^{-\frac{1}{2}} - x^2\right) + \mu^2\left(\dfrac{x^{\frac{7}{2}}}{4} - \dfrac{4}{3}x + \dfrac{25}{12}x^{-\frac{1}{2}} - x^{-\frac{3}{2}}\right) + \ldots$

725. $y = 1 + \mu\,(x^2 - x) - \dfrac{\mu^2}{6}\,x\,(x - 1)^3 + \ldots$

14. Linear Systems with Constant Coefficients.

726. $x = C_1 e^t + C_2 e^{5t}, \quad y = -C_1 e^t + 3C_2 e^{5t}.$ **727.** $x = C_1 e^{-t} + C_2 e^{3t},$
$y = 2C_1 e^{-t} - 2C_2 e^{3t}.$ **728.** $x = 2C_1 e^{3t} - 4C_2 e^{-3t}, \quad y = C_1 e^{3t} + C_2 e^{-3t}.$
729. $x = e^{2t}\,(C_1 \cos t + C_2 \sin t), \quad y = e^{2t}\,[(C_1 + C_2)\cos t + (C_2 - C_1)\sin t].$
730. $x = e^t\,(C_1 \cos 3t + C_2 \sin 3t), \qquad y = e^t\,(C_1 \sin 3t - C_2 \cos 3t).$
731. $x = (2C_2 - C_1)\cos 2t - (2C_1 + C_2)\sin 2t, \; y = C_1 \cos 2t + C_2 \sin 2t.$
732. $x = (C_1 + C_2 t)\,e^{3t}, \; y = (C_1 + C_2 + C_2 t)\,e^{3t}.$ **733.** $x = (C_1 + C_2 t)\,e^t.$
$y = (2C_1 - C_2 + 2C_2 t)\,e^t.$ **734.** $x = (C_1 + 2C_2 t)\,e^{-t}, \; y = (C_1 + C_2 + 2C_2 t)\,e^{-t}.$
735. $x = (C_1 + 3C_2 t)\,e^{2t}, \quad y = (C_2 - C_1 - 3C_2 t)\,e^{2t}.$ **736.** $x = C_1 e^t +$
$+ C_2 e^{2t} + C_3 e^{-t}, \qquad y = C_1 e^t - 3C_3 e^{-t}, \qquad z = C_1 e^t + C_2 e^{2t} - 5C_3 e^{-t}.$
737. $x = C_1 + 3C_2 e^{2t}, \; y = -2C_2 e^{2t} + C_3 e^{-t}, \; z = C_1 + C_2 e^{2t} - 2C_3 e^{-t}.$
738. $x = C_2 e^{2t} + C_3 e^{3t}, \; y = C_1 e^t + C_2 e^{2t}, \quad z = C_1 e^t + C_2 e^{2t} + C_3 e^{3t}.$
739. $x = C_1 e^t + C_2 e^{2t} + C_3 e^{5t}, \qquad y = C_1 e^t - 2C_2 e^{2t} + C_3 e^{5t}.$
$z = -C_1 e^t - 3C_2 e^{2t} + 3C_3 e^{5t}.$ **740.** $x = C_1 e^t + C_3 e^{-t}, \; y = C_1 e^t + C_2 e^{2t},$
$z = 2C_2 e^{2t} - C_3 e^{-t}.$ **741.** $x = e^t\,(2C_2 \sin 2t + 2C_3 \cos 2t),$
$y = e^t\,(C_1 - C_2 \cos 2t + C_3 \sin 2t), \; z = e^t\,(-C_1 - 3C_2 \cos 2t + 3C_3 \sin 2t).$
742. $x = C_1 e^{2t} + e^{3t}\,(C_2 \cos t + C_3 \sin t), \quad y = e^{3t}\,[(C_2 + C_3)\cos t +$
$+ (C_3 - C_2)\sin t], \; z = C_1 e^{2t} + e^{3t}\,[(2C_2 - C_3)\cos t + (2C_3 + C_2)\sin t].$
743. $x = C_2 \cos t + (C_2 + 2C_3)\sin t, \; y = 2C_1 e^t + C_2 \cos t + (C_2 + 2C_3)\sin t,$
$z = C_1 e^t + C_3 \cos t - (C_2 + C_3)\sin t.$ **744.** $x = C_1 e^{2t} + (C_2 + C_3)\,e^{3t},$
$y = C_1 e^{2t} + C_2 e^{3t}, \; z = C_1 e^{2t} + C_3 e^{3t}.$ **745.** $x = C_1 + C_2 e^t, \; y = 3C_1 + C_3 e^t,$
$z = -C_1 + (C_2 - C_3)\,e^t.$ **746.** $x = C_1 e^{3t} + C_2 e^{-t}, \quad y = -C_1 e^{3t} +$
$+ (C_2 + 2C_3)\,e^{-t}, \; z = -3C_1 e^{3t} + C_3 e^{-t}.$ **747.** $x = C_1 e^{2t} + C_3 e^{-5t},$
$y = C_2 e^{2t} + 3C_3 e^{-5t}, \; z = (C_1 - 2C_2)\,e^{2t} + 2C_3 e^{-5t}.$ **748.** $x = (C_1 +$
$+ C_2 t)\,e^t + C_3 e^{2t}, \; y = (C_1 - 2C_2 + C_2 t)\,e^t, \; z = (C_1 - C_2 + C_2 t)\,e^t + C_3 e^{2t}.$
749. $x = (C_2 + C_3 t)\,e^{-t}, \qquad y = 2C_1 e^t - (2C_2 + C_3 + 2C_3 t)\,e^{-t},$
$z = C_1 e^t - (C_2 + C_3 + C_3 t)\,e^{-t}.$ **750.** $x = C_1 + C_2 t + 4C_3 e^{3t},$
$y = C_2 - 2C_1 - 2C_2 t + 4C_3 e^{3t}, \qquad z = C_1 - C_2 + C_2 t + C_3 e^{3t}.$
751. $x = (C_1 + C_3 t)\,e^t, \; y = (C_2 + 2C_3 t)\,e^t, \; z = (C_1 - C_2 - C_3 - C_3 t)\,e^t.$
752. $x = (C_1 + C_2 t + C_3 t^2)\,e^{2t}, \; y = [2C_1 - C_2 + (2C_2 - 2C_3)\,t + 2C_3 t^2]\,e^{2t},$
$z = [C_1 - C_2 + 2C_3 + (C_2 - 2C_3)\,t + C_3 t^2]\,e^{2t}.$ **753.** $x = 3C_1 e^t +$
$+ 3C_2 e^{-t} + C_3 \cos t + C_4 \sin t, \; y = C_1 e^t + C_2 e^{-t} + C_3 \cos t + C_4 \sin t.$
754. $x = -2e^t\,(C_1 + C_2 + C_2 t) - 2e^{-t}\,(C_3 - C_4 + C_4 t), \quad y = e^t\,(C_1 +$
$+ C_2 t) + e^{-t}\,(C_3 + C_4 t).$ **755.** $x = e^t\,(C_1 \cos t + C_2 \sin t) +$
$+ e^{-t}\,(C_3 \cos t + C_4 \sin t), \qquad y = e^t\,(C_1 \sin t - C_2 \cos t) +$
$+ e^{-t}\,(C_4 \cos t - C_3 \sin t).$

756.. $x = C_1 e^t + C_2 e^{-t} + C_3 e^{2t} + C_5 e^{-2t},$

$y = C_1 e^t + C_2 e^{-t} + C_4 e^{2t} + C_6 e^{-2t}, \; z = C_1 e^t + C_2 e^{-t} - (C_3 + C_4) e^{2t} -$
$- (C_5 + C_6) e^{-2t}.$ **757** $x = 3C_1 e^t + C_2 e_6^{-t}, \quad y = C_1 e^t + C_2 e^{-t}.$
758. $x = C_1 e^t + C_2 e^{-t} + 2C_3 e^{-2t}, \; y = 2C_1 e^t + C_3 e^{-2t}.$ **759.** $x = 3C e^t,$
$y = C e^{-t}.$ **760.** $x = - 2C_2 e^{3t} + C_3 e^t, \qquad y = C_1 e^{-t} + C_2 e^{3t}.$
761. $x = 2C_1 e^{2t} + 2C_2 e^{-2t} + 2C_3 \cos 2t + 2C_4 \sin 2t, \quad y = 3C_1 e^{2t} -$

$- 3C_2 e^{-2t} - C_3 \sin 2t + C_4 \cos 2t.$ **762.** $x = C_1 e^{\frac{t}{2}} - 4C_2 e^{-2t},$

$y = C_1 e^{\frac{t}{2}} + C_2 e^{-2t}.$ **763.** $x = (C_1 + C_2 t) e^t + C_3 e^{-t}, \quad y = (-2C_1 -$
$- C_2 - 2C_2 t) e^t - 4C_3 e^{-t}.$ **764.** $x = C_1 e^t + C_2 e^{-t} + C_3 e^{2t} + C_4 e^{-2t},$
$y = C_1 e^t + 5C_2 e^{-t} + 2C_3 e^{2t} + 2C_4 e^{-2t}.$ **765.** $x = C_1 + C_2 e^t + C_3 \cos t + C_4 \sin t,$
$y = - C_1 - C_2 e^t + \left(\frac{3}{5} C_4 - \frac{4}{5} C_3 \right) \cos t - \left(\frac{3}{5} C_3 + \frac{4}{5} C_4 \right) \sin t.$
766. $x = C_1 e^t + C_2 e^{-t} + t e^t - t^2 - 2, \; y = C_1 e^t - C_2 e^{-t} + (t - 1) e^t - 2t.$
767. $x = C_1 e^{2t} + C_2 e^{-t} - 2 \sin t - \cos t, \; y = 2C_1 e^{2t} - C_2 e^{-t} + \sin t + 3 \cos t.$
768. $x = C_1 e^t + 2C_2 e^{4t} + 3 e^{5t}, \qquad y = - C_1 e^t + C_2 e^{4t} + e^{5t}.$
769. $x = C_1 e^{-t} + 4C_2 e^{2t} + 3 e^{-2t}, \qquad y = C_1 e^{-t} + C_2 e^{2t} + 4 e^{-2t}.$
770. $x = C_1 e^{2t} + C_2 e^{3t} + (t + 1) e^{2t}, \qquad y = - 2C_1 e^{2t} - C_2 e^{3t} - 2t e^{2t}.$
771. $x = (C_1 + 2C_2 t) e^t - 3, \qquad y = (C_1 + C_2 + 2C_2 t) e^t - 2.$
772. $x = C_1 e^{2t} + 3C_2 e^{4t} - e^{-t} - 4 e^{3t}, \; y = C_1 e^{2t} + C_2 e^{4t} - 2 e^{-t} - 2 e^{3t}.$
773. $x = C_1 e^{2t} + C_2 e^{-2t} - \frac{1}{4} - \frac{2}{3} e^t, \; y = C_1 e^{2t} - 3C_2 e^{-2t} - \frac{3}{4} - e^t.$
774. $x = C_1 e^{-t} + 2C_2 e^{2t} - \cos t + 3 \sin t, \; y = - C_1 e^{-t} + C_2 e^{2t} + 2 \cos t - \sin t.$
775. $x = 4C_1 e^t + C_2 e^{-2t} - 4t e^t, \qquad y = C_1 e^t + C_2 e^{-2t} - (t - 1) e^t.$
776. $x = C_1 e^{3t} + 3t^2 + 2t + C_2, \qquad y = - C_1 e^{3t} + 6t^2 - 2t + 2C_2 - 2.$
777. $x = 2C_1 e^{2t} + C_2 e^{-3t} - (12t + 13) e^t, \; y = C_1 e^{2t} - 2C_2 e^{-3t} - (8t + 6) e^t.$
778. $x = 2C_1 e^{8t} - 2C_2 - 6t + 1, \qquad y = 3C_1 e^{8t} + C_2 + 3t.$
779. $x = 3C_1 e^t + C_2 e^{-t} + 3 \sin t, \quad y = C_1 e^t + C_2 e^{-t} - \cos t + 2 \sin t.$
780. $x = C_1 e^{-t} + C_2 e^{5t} - 3 e^t + 2t - \frac{13}{5}, \qquad y = - C_1 e^{-t} + C_2 e^{5t} +$

$+ e^t - 3t + \frac{12}{5}.$ **781.** $x = (C_1 + C_2 t - t^2) e^t, \quad y = [C_1 - C_2 +$
$+ (C_2 + 2) t - t^2] e^t.$ **782.** $x = C_1 e^t + 3C_2 e^{2t} + \cos t - 2 \sin t,$
$y = C_1 e^t + 2C_2 e^{2t} + 2 \cos t - 2 \sin t.$ **733.** $x = C_1 e^t + C_2 e^{3t} + t e^t - e^{4t},$
$y = - C_1 e^t + C_2 e^{3t} - (t + 1) e^t - 2 e^{4t}.$ **734.** $x = C_1 \cos 2t - C_2 \sin 2t + 2t + 2,$
$y = (C_1 + 2C_2) \cos 2t + (2C_1 - C_2) \sin 2t + 10t.$ **735.** $x = C_1 e^t +$
$+ C_2 e^{3t} + e^t (2 \cos t - \sin t), \qquad y = C_1 e^t - C_2 e^{3t} + e^t (3 \cos t + \sin t).$
786. $x = C_1 \cos t + C_2 \sin t + \operatorname{tg} t, \qquad y = - C_1 \sin t + C_2 \cos t + 2.$
787. $x = C_1 e^t + 2C_2 e^{2t} - e^t \ln (e^{2t} + 1) + 2 e^{2t} \operatorname{arctg} e^t, \qquad y = C_1 e^t +$
$+ 3C_2 e^{2t} - e^t \ln (e^{2t} + 1) + 3 e^{2t} \operatorname{arctg} e^t.$ **738.** $x = C_1 + 2C_2 e^{-t} +$
$+ 2 e^{-t} \ln |e^t - 1|, \qquad y = - 2C_1 - 3C_2 e^{-t} - 3 e^{-t} \ln |e^t - 1|.$
789. $x = C_1 \cos t + C_2 \sin t + t (\cos t + \sin t) + (\cos t - \sin t) \ln |\cos t|,$
$y = (C_1 - C_2) \cos t + (C_1 + C_2) \sin t + 2 \cos t \ln |\cos t| + 2t \sin t.$

790. $x = \left(C_1 + 2C_2 t - 8t^{\frac{5}{2}} \right) e^t, \; y = \left(C_1 + 2C_2 t - C_2 - 8t^{\frac{5}{2}} + 10t^{\frac{3}{2}} \right) e^t.$

15. Lyapunov Stability.

791. Stable. 792. Stable. 793. Stable. 794. Unstable.

795. Unstable. 796. Stable. 797. The solution (0,0) is un-

stable; the solution (1,2) is stable. 798. The solutions

(1,2), (2,1) are both unstable. 799. The solution (2,1) is

unstable; the solution (2,-1) is stable. 800. If k is an

integer, the solutions $x = 2k\pi$, $y = 0$ are unstable, but the

solutions $x = (2k + 1)\pi$, $y = 0$ are stable. 801. Stable.

802. Stable. 803. No, to both questions. 806. Unstable.

807. Stable. 808. Stable. 809. Stable. 810 Stable.

16. Singular Points.

811. Saddle. 812. Node. 813. Focus. 814. Node.

815. Saddle. 816. Center. 817. Degenerate node. 818. Node.

819. Singular node. 820. Focus. 821. Node. 822. Degenerate

node. 823. Focus. 824. Saddle. 825. Center. 826. Degenerate

node. 827, 828. The singular points fill out a straight line.

829. The point (-2,-1) is a node. 830. The point (1,-2) is a

focus. 831. The point (3,6) is a degenerate node. 832. The

point (2,1) is a saddle; the point (-2,1) is a node. 835. The

point (4,2) is a node; the point (-2,-1) is a focus. 836. The point (1,0) is a saddle; the point (0,2) is a degenerate node.

837. The point (1,0) is a singular node; the point (-1,0) is a saddle. 838. The point (0,1) is a center; the point (0,-1) is a saddle. 839. The point (2,2) is a node; the point (0,-2) is a saddle; (-1-1), a focus. 840. The points (1,0) and (-1,0) are saddles; the points (0,1) and (0,-1) are centers. 841. Singular points as follows: (1,1) is a saddle; (1,-1) is a node; (2,2), (-2,2) are foci. 842. (0,0) is a focus; (0,8) is a saddle; (3,-1) is a saddle; (7,1) is a node. 843. In the upper half-plane y > 0, the integral curves are arranged somewhat like those around a saddle point; in the lower half-plane y < 0, like a node. 844. A single curve has a simple cusp at the origin (0,0). The other curves do not touch the singular point. 845. In the upper half-plane y > 0, all the integral curves terminate in the singular point; in the lower half-plane y < 0, none does. 846. Two integral curves pass through the singular point, where they are mutually tangent. The remaining curves form a saddle-point configuration. 847. In the upper half-plane y > 0, the curves do not enter the singular point. In the third quadrant y < 0, x < 0, the curves behave like

those near a degenerate node. In the fourth quadrant

$y < 0$, $x > 0$, the curves form a saddle-point configuration

17. Problems in the Theory of Oscillations.

851. There are two cases to consider. If $n^2 > 4km$, the solution is $x = \dfrac{v_0}{2\gamma}(e^{(-\alpha+\gamma)t} - e^{(-\alpha-\gamma)t})$, $\alpha = \dfrac{n}{2m}$, $\gamma = \dfrac{\sqrt{n^2 - 4km}}{2m}$. If $n^2 < 4km$, the solution is $x = \dfrac{v_0}{\beta}e^{-\alpha t}\sin\beta t$, $\alpha = \dfrac{n}{2m}$, $\beta = \dfrac{\sqrt{4km - n^2}}{2m}$.

852. $n = \sqrt{4km}$. 860. $\dfrac{1}{2\pi}\sqrt{K\left(\dfrac{1}{I_1} + \dfrac{1}{I_2}\right)}$.

861. $A = \dfrac{B}{1 - \dfrac{m}{k}\omega^2}$. 862. $I = \dfrac{V}{R}\left(1 - e^{-\frac{R}{L}t}\right)$. 863. $I = \dfrac{V}{R}e^{-\frac{t}{RC}}$.

864. $I = \dfrac{q}{RC}e^{-\frac{t}{RC}}$. 865. $I = \dfrac{q}{\omega CL}e^{-\frac{Rt}{2L}}\sin\omega t$, $CR^2 < 4L$, $\omega = \dfrac{\sqrt{4CL - R^2C^2}}{2LC}$. 866. $I = A\sin(\omega t - \varphi)$, $A = \dfrac{V}{\sqrt{R^2 + \omega^2 L^2}}$, $\varphi = \text{arctg}\dfrac{\omega L}{R}$. 867. $I = A\sin(\omega t - \varphi)$,

$A = \dfrac{V}{\sqrt{R^2 + \left(\omega L - \dfrac{1}{\omega C}\right)^2}}$, $\varphi = \text{arctg}\dfrac{\omega L - \dfrac{1}{\omega C}}{R}$; $\max A = \dfrac{V}{R}$

where $\omega^2 = \dfrac{1}{LC}$. 868. $I = A\sin(\omega t - \varphi)$, $A = \dfrac{V}{\sqrt{R^2 + \left(\dfrac{\omega L}{1 - \omega^2 LC}\right)^2}}$;

the maximum value of A is V/R; this value occurs for $\omega = 0$

and $\omega = \infty$; the minimum value of A is 0; this value occurs

for $\omega^2 = (LC)^{-1}$. 870. $x(\pi) = -4$. The amplitude decreases by

1 in every half oscillation. 871. $l\ddot{\varphi} + g\sin\varphi = 0$.

872. $ml\ddot{\varphi} + kl^2\dot{\varphi}|\dot{\varphi}| + mg\sin\varphi = 0$. 873. $\dfrac{d^2 I_L}{dt^2} + \dfrac{R}{L}\dfrac{dI_L}{dt} - \dfrac{1}{CL}f\left(M\dfrac{dI_L}{dt}\right) + \dfrac{I_L}{CL} = 0$;

if $RC < M f'(0)$, the equilibrium $I_L(t) = f(0)$ is unstable.

874. In the latter case, the relation $F'(0) < 0$ holds, and

there is a limit cycle in the phase plane. 892. $a < -1/2$;

$a > -1/2$.

18. Dependence of Solutions on Initial Conditions and on
Parameters.

895. Smaller than 0.03. 896. Smaller than 0.1($-1 + \exp 2T$).

897. $\left| \tilde{x} - x \right| + \left| \tilde{y} - y \right| < 0.0012$. 898. The error is less than

0.003. 899. The error is less than 0.034.

900. $e^{2x} - x - 1$. 901. $t^2 \ln t + 2t^2 - 2t$.

902. $\dfrac{e^{2t}}{36} - \dfrac{e^{-2t}}{4} + \left(\dfrac{2}{9} - \dfrac{t}{3}\right)e^{-t} + \dfrac{1}{8}$.   905. $x = \sin t +$

$+ \mu\left(\dfrac{1}{6} - \dfrac{1}{2}\cos 2t\right) + \mu^2\left(\dfrac{1}{2}\sin t - \dfrac{1}{6}\sin 3t\right) + O(\mu^3)$. 906. $x = \cos 2t +$

$+ \mu\left(\dfrac{1}{10} - \dfrac{1}{22}\cos 4t\right) + \mu^2\left(\dfrac{17}{110}\cos 2t + \dfrac{1}{682}\cos 6t\right) + O(\mu^3)$.

907. $x = \mu\cos t + \mu^3\left(-\dfrac{3}{8}\cos t + \dfrac{1}{24}\cos 3t\right) + O(\mu^5)$. 908. $x_1 = 1 +$

$+ \mu\sin t - \dfrac{\mu^2}{4}(1 + \cos 2t) + O(\mu^3)$, $x_2 = -1 - \dfrac{\mu}{3}\sin t +$

$+ \dfrac{\mu^2}{36}\left(1 - \dfrac{1}{3}\cos 2t\right) + O(\mu^3)$. 909. $x_1 = -\dfrac{\mu}{3}\sin 2t + \dfrac{\mu^3}{648}\left(\sin 2t -\right.$

$\left.- \dfrac{1}{35}\sin 6t\right) + O(\mu^5)$, $x_2 = \pi - \dfrac{\mu}{5}\sin 2t - \dfrac{\mu^3}{1000}\left(\dfrac{1}{5}\sin 2t - \dfrac{1}{111}\sin 6t\right) +$

$+ O(\mu^5)$.   910. $x = \dfrac{1}{8}\sin t + \dfrac{1}{3}\sin 2t - \dfrac{1}{8}\sin 3t + O(\mu)$.

911. $x = 2\mu^{\frac{1}{3}}\sin t - \mu\left(\dfrac{1}{12}\sin t + \dfrac{1}{4}\sin 3t\right) + O\left(\mu^{\frac{5}{3}}\right)$. 912. $x = C\cos \tau +$

$+ C^2\left(\dfrac{1}{2} - \dfrac{1}{3}\cos \tau - \dfrac{1}{6}\cos 2\tau\right) + O(C^3)$, $\tau = t\left(1 - \dfrac{5}{12}C^2 + O(C^3)\right) + C_2$.

913. $x = C\cos \tau + \dfrac{C^3}{192}(\cos \tau - \cos 3\tau) + O(C^5)$, $\tau = t\left(1 - \dfrac{C^2}{16} +\right.$

$\left.+ O(C^4)\right) + C_2$.   914. $x = 2\cos \tau - \dfrac{\mu}{4}\sin 3\tau + O(\mu^2)$,

$\tau = t\left(1 - \dfrac{\mu^2}{16} + O(\mu^4)\right) + C$.

19. Non-Linear Systems.

921. $y = C_2 e^{C_1 x^2}$, $\quad z = \dfrac{1}{2 C_1 C_2} e^{-C_1 x^2}$. $\qquad$ **922.** $y = C_2 e^{C_1 x}$,

$z = x + \dfrac{C_2}{C_1} e^{C_1 x}$. $\qquad$ **923.** $y = \dfrac{x + C_1}{x + C_2}$, $\quad z = \dfrac{(C_2 - C_1)\, x}{(x + C_2)^2}$.

924. $y = C_2 e^{C_1 x^2}$, $z = \dfrac{2 C_1}{C_2} x e^{-C_1 x^2}$. **925.** $y = -\dfrac{1}{C_1} + \dfrac{C_1}{2}(x + C_2) - $

$- \dfrac{C_1}{4}(x + C_2)^2$, $z = \dfrac{C_1}{4}(x + C_2)^2 + \dfrac{1}{C_1}$. **926.** $y = C_1 z$, $x = 2y - z + C_2$.

927. $x^2 - y^2 = C_1$, $\quad x + y = C_2 z$. $\qquad$ **928.** $x - y = C_1(y - z)$,

$(x + y + z)(x - y)^2 = C_2$. **929.** $x + z = C_1$, $(x + y + z)(y - 3x - z) = C_2$.

930. $x^2 - z^2 = C_1$, $y^2 - u^2 = C_2$, $(x + z) = C_3(u + y)$. **931.** $x + z = C_1$,

$y + u = C_2$, $\quad (x - z)^2 + (y - u)^2 = C_3$. $\qquad$ **932.** $x^2 - 2y = C_1$,

$6xy - 2x^3 - 3z^2 = C_2$. **933.** $y^2 + z^2 = C_1$, $x - yz = C_2$. **934.** $x = C_1 y$,

$xy - z = C_2 x$. **935.** $x = C_1 y$, $xy - 2\sqrt{z^2 + 1} = C_2$. **936.** $y = C_1 z$,

$x - y^2 - z^2 = C_2 z$. **937.** $y^2 + z^2 = C_1$, $x(y - z) = C_2$. **938.** $xz = C_1$,

$xy + z^2 = C_2$. **939.** $x + z - y = C_1$, $\ln|x| + \dfrac{z}{y} = C_2$. **940.** $x^2 + y^2 + $

$+ z^2 = C_1$, $yz = C_2 x$. $\qquad$ **941.** 1: yes; 2: no. $\quad$ **942.** 1: no; 2: yes.

943. Yes. $\quad$ **944.** Dependent.

20. First Order Partial Differential Equations.

946. $F(x^2 - y^2, x - y + z) = 0$. **947.** $F\left(e^{-x} - y^{-1}, z + \dfrac{x - \ln|y|}{e^{-x} - y^{-1}}\right) = 0$.

948. $F\left(x^2 - 4z, \dfrac{(x + y)^2}{x}\right) = 0$. $\qquad$ **949.** $F\left(x^2 + y^2, \dfrac{z}{x}\right) = 0$.

950. $F\left(\dfrac{x^2}{y}, xy - \dfrac{3z}{x}\right) = 0$. **951.** $F\left(\dfrac{1}{x + y} + \dfrac{1}{z}, \dfrac{1}{x - y} + \dfrac{1}{z}\right) = 0$.

952. $F(x^2 + y^4, y(z + \sqrt{z^2 + 1})) = 0$. **953.** $F\left(\dfrac{1}{x} - \dfrac{1}{y}, \ln|xy| - \dfrac{z^2}{2}\right) = 0$.

954. $F\left(x^2 + y^2, \operatorname{arctg}\dfrac{x}{y} + (z + 1)\, e^{-z}\right) = 0$. $\qquad$ **955.** $F(z^2 - y^2,$

$x^2 + (y - z)^2) = 0$. **956.** $F\left(\dfrac{z}{x}, 2x - 4z - y^2\right) = 0$. **957.** $F(z - \ln|x|,$

$2x(z - 1) - y^2) = 0$. **958.** $F(\operatorname{tg} z + \operatorname{ctg} x, 2y + 2\operatorname{tg} z \cdot \operatorname{ctg} x + \operatorname{ctg}^2 x) = 0$.

959. $F\left(\dfrac{x + y + z}{(x - y)^2}, (x - y)(x + y - 2z)\right) = 0$. **960.** $F((x - y)(z + 1),$

$(x + y)(z - 1)) = 0$. $\quad$ **961.** $F\left(u(x - y), u(y - z), \dfrac{x + y + z}{u^2}\right) = $

962. $F\left(\dfrac{x}{y}, xy - 2u, \dfrac{z + u - xy}{x}\right) = 0$. **963.** $F\left(\dfrac{x - y}{z}, (2u + x + y)z,\right.$

$\left.\dfrac{u - x - y}{z^2}\right) = 0$. $\qquad$ **964.** $y^2 - x^2 - \ln\sqrt{y^2 - x^2} = z - \ln|y|$.

965. $2x^2(y + 1) = y^2 + 4z - 1$. **966.** $(x + 2y)^2 = 2x(z + xy)$.

967. $\sqrt{\dfrac{z}{y^3}}\,\sin x = \sin\sqrt{\dfrac{z}{y}}$.   968. $2xy + 1 = x + 3y + z^{-1}$.

969. $x - 2y = x^2 + y^2 + z$.   970. $2x^2 - y^2 - z^2 = a^2$.

971. $[(y^2z - 2)^2 - x^2 + z]\,y^2z = 1$.   972. $x^2 + z^2 = 5\,(xz - y)$.

973. $3\,(x + y + z)^2 = x^2 + y^2 + z^2$.   974. $xz = (xz - y - x + 2z)^2$.

975. $(1 + yz)^3 = 3yz\,(1 + yz - x) + y^3$.   976. $x + y + z = 0$.

977. $2\,(x^3 - 4z^3 - 3yz)^2 = 9\,(y + z^2)^3$. 978. $(x - y)\,(3x + y + 4z) = 4z$.

979. $xz + y^2 = 0$.   980. $z = xy + f(y/x)$, where f is any

differentiable function satisfying $f(1) = 0$.

981. $F(x^2 - y^2,\ 2x^2 + z^2) = 0$.   981. $F(x^2 - y^2,\ 2x^2 + z^2) = 0$.

983. $F(2x - z,\ x - y) = 0$.   984. $(x - y)^2 + (z - x - y)^2 = 4$.

985. $F\!\left(\dfrac{y - b}{x - a},\ \dfrac{z - c}{x - a}\right) = 0$.   986. $F\!\left(\dfrac{x^2}{y},\ \dfrac{z}{y}\right) = 0$.   987. $z = Cxy^2$.

988. No solution.   989. $z = 0$.   990. No solution.   991. $x^3 y^2 z = C$.

992. $z = y^2 - xy$.   993. $x^2 yz = C - x^3$; $x = 0$.

Appendix A

LINEAR DIFFERENTIAL EQUATIONS
WITH CONSTANT COEFFICIENTS

A complete theory of linear differential equations with

constant coefficients is given in this appendix. (For Laplace

transform methods, see Appendix B.) To expound the present

theory, the following lemmas are needed.

(1) The theorem of the mean. If $h(x)$ has a derivative

everywhere, and if $Dh(x) \equiv h'(x)$ is identically 0, $a \leq x \leq b$,

then $h(x)$ is constant on the range (a,b): $h(x) = c$, $a \leq x \leq b$.

(2) The euclidean algorithm. If f_1, f_2 are polynomials

in a single indeterminate with no (nonconstant) common factor,

there are two polynomials g_1, g_2 such that $f_1 g_1 + f_2 g_2 = 1$.

For example: $(x - \alpha_1) + (x - \alpha_2)(-1) = \alpha_2 - \alpha_1$. If $\alpha_2 \neq \alpha_1$,

divide both sides by $\alpha_2 - \alpha_1$.

The general theory below explains the unifying principles

underlying the examples:

(1) Solve $y' - 3y = 0$.

Solution: $y_0 = e^{3x}$ is a solution; set $z = y/y_0 = ye^{-3x}$.

Then $z' = e^{-3x}[y' - 3y] = 0$. Hence if y is a solution,

the theorem of the mean shows that $z = \text{const}$; $ye^{-3x} = c$,

$y = ce^{3x}$.

(2) Every solution of $w' - aw$ is given by $w = ce^{ax}$

for some constant c.

(3) Solve $y'' - 3y' - 4y = 0$. This is a second-order

equation. See the first-order examples $(1,2)$.

Try to adjust m so that e^{mx} is a solution:

$e^{mx} (m^2 - 3m - 4) = 0$. This is satisfied by $m = 4$,

$m = -1$. It can be proved (see below) that <u>every</u>

solution can be written $y = c_1 e^{4x} + c_2 e^{-x}$.

(4) Solve $y'' - 3y' - 4y = 3e^{4x}$. The function e^{4x}

satisfies (3), but the function $c_3 xe^{4x}$ satisfies (4)

if c_3 is properly chosen. Every solution of (4) has

the form $y = c_1 e^{4x} + c_2 e^{-c} + \dfrac{1}{5} xe^{4x}$.

(5) Solve $[D^2 + 3D + 3] y = 0$. The operator can be written

$(D + \dfrac{3}{2})^2 + \dfrac{3}{4} = (D - \alpha)^2 + \beta^2$ with $a = -\dfrac{3}{2}$, $\beta = \dfrac{1}{2}\sqrt{3}$.

Every solution of (5) has the form

$y = e^{-3x/2} [c_1 \cos (\dfrac{1}{2}\sqrt{3} x) + c_2 \sin (\dfrac{1}{2}\sqrt{3} x)]$

(6) $[D^2 + 3D + 3] y = 64 x^2 \sin x$ has one solution of the

form $y_0 = (c_3 + c_4 x + c_5 x^2) \sin x + (c_6 + c_7 x + c_8 x^2) \cos$

Every solution y can be written as

$y_0 + e^{-3x/2} (c_1 \cos \sqrt{3} x/2 + c_2 \sin \sqrt{3} x/2)$

(7) $[D^2 + 3D + 3] y = 8e^{-3x/2} \cos (\frac{1}{2} \sqrt{3} x)$ has one solution

of the form $y_o = e^{-3x/2} \cos (\frac{1}{2} \sqrt{3} x) \{c_3 + c_4 x\}$

$+ e^{-3x/2} \sin (\frac{1}{2} \sqrt{3} x) \{c_5 + c_6 x\}$.

The General Theory.

This treatment is based on simpler principles than the
exposition in some books. See especially theorem 1. In particular,
we establish a complete theory without needing the Wronskian, or
even linear dependence.

We mention that if all solutions of $[f(D)] y = 0$ are known,
there is an integral formula for solving $[f(D)] y = F(x)$.

The theory is presented in logical form. In some cases proofs
that depend on inductive arguments are omitted or only sketched.
Aside from abbreviations of this kind, the theory is complete. To
maintain the elementary point of view, complex arithmetic is eschewed.
After a section on motivation, the argument begins. First there
is the decomposition theorem, that reduces the problem of solving a
d.e. to the problem of solving several simpler ones:

$$\{D - a\}^p y = 0 \; ; \quad \{(D - \alpha)^2 + \beta^2\}^p y = 0 \; .$$

Finally all solutions of the latter are found. Some complements of
the theory and proofs are given at the end.

Definition. By <u>d.e.</u> we shall mean an ordinary linear d.e. with constant coefficients; the forcing function is 0 except where the context specifies otherwise. Thus it makes sense to seek a solution of the d.e. on some finite interval. It will turn out that every solution of such a d.e. can be defined (extended) over the doubly infinite interval.

Examples of d.e.'s are

$$y' = y, \ y' = a \ y, \ y'' + y = 0; \ y'' - 3y' + 2y = 0 \ .$$

The first two equations are familiar enough so that the functions e^x, e^{ax} will be recognized as solutions (a is a constant).

This suggests that possibly e^{ax} may be a solution of the others, if the constant a is properly chosen. Testing this possibility, we come in the two cases to the algebraic equations

$$a^2 + 1 = 0 \ ; \quad a^2 - 3 \ a + 2 = 0 \quad .$$

Putting aside the imposibility of satisfying the first of these equations, we rescue at least the notational advantage of writing the four equations (in the examples above) in the respective forms

$$Dy = y, \ Dy = a \ y; \ \left[D^2 + 1\right] y = 0 \ ; \ \left[D^2 - 3D + 2\right] y = 0 \ .$$

We now see that the theory we are setting out to establish can be concisely stated as follows: let f be any polynomial with real, constant coefficients. Find all solutions of the d.e.

$$\left[f(D)\right] y = 0 \quad .$$

Some preliminary lemmas

Lemma 1. Every solution of a d.e. has as many derivatives as you please. For example, if y satisfies $y' + 3y = 0$, then y' exists. But then, $y' = -3y$, and $-3y$ has a derivative. So y' must have a derivative, that is, y has a second derivative.

Lemma 2. Let f_1, f_2 be two polynomials with no (nonconstant) common factor. Then every solution of

(1) $\left[f_1(d) \cdot f_2(D) \right] y = 0$ is expressible as the sum of two terms, one a solution of $\left[f_1(D) \right] y = 0$ and the other, a solution of $\left[f_2(D) \right] y = 0$.

Proof. Since the polynomials f_1, f_2 are relatively prime, there exist other polynomials g_1, g_2 such that

(2) $f_1 g_1 + f_2 g_2 = 1$.

Let y be some solution of (1) $\left[f_1 f_2 \right] y = 0$. It is required to show that y_1, y_2 exist so that (1°) $f_1(D) y_1 = 0$, $f_2(D) y_2 = 0$;

$$(2^{\circ}) \quad y = y_1 + y_2 .$$

The idea of the demonstration is based on (2). We try

$$y_1 = \left[f_2(D) g_2(D) \right] y, \quad y_2 = \left[f_1(D) g_1(D) \right] y .$$

These formulas satisfy the requirements. It must first be shown that the formulas have a meaning; see lemma 1. Second, it is necessary to know that multiplication of polynomials is commutative, that is that the formula

$$[f_1 \ f_2 \ g_2] \ y = [g_2] \ ([f_1 \ f_2] \ y)$$

is correct. The validity of this formula depends crucially on the fact that the polynomials have constant coefficients, i.e. that $D(\text{const. } y) = \text{const. } Dy$. ‖

In case $f(D)$ has multiple factors, lemma 2 does at least show how to reduce the problem of solving $[f(D)] \ y = 0$ to a series of simpler problems. The lemma will also enable us to assert at some point that we have found all solutions of a given d.e.

Lemma 3. If y is a solution of the d.e. $[f(D)] \ y = 0$, then $z = y \ e^{-\alpha x}$ is a solution of $[f(D + \alpha)] \ z = 0$.

For example, if y is a solution of $[D^2 - 3D + 2] \ y = 0$, then (with $\alpha = 2$) solutions e^{bx} of $[f(D + 2)] \ z \equiv [D^2 + D] \ z = 0$ are $z = y \ e^{-2x}$, i.e. $z = 1$, $z = e^{-x}$.

The proof of lemma 3 is based on the fundamental formula

$$[D + \alpha] \ (y \ e^{-\alpha x}) = e^{-\alpha x} \ \{Dy - \alpha y + \alpha y\} = e^{-\alpha x} \ Dy \ .$$

Lemma 4. The d.e. $y'' + \beta^2 \ y \equiv [D^2 + \beta^2] \ y = 0$ has solutions $y = \cos \beta x, \ y = \sin \beta x$.

Lemma 4 identifies $e^{\pm i \beta x}$ with $\cos \beta x, \ \sin \beta x$, at least formally. We do not claim to have all solutions at this point.

Lemma 5. The second-order d.e. $[(D - \alpha)^2 + \beta^2] y = 0$ has

solutions $y = e^{\alpha x} \cos \beta x$, $y = e^{\alpha x} \sin \beta x$.

This lemma follows directly from lemmas 3, 4. It identifies

(in a formal sense) the functions $e^{(\alpha \pm i\beta) x}$ with the functions

$e^{\alpha x} \cos \beta x$; $e^{\alpha x} \sin \beta x$.

Theorem 1. Let y be any solution of the d. e. $[D^2 + 1] y = 0$.

Then corresponding constants c_1, c_2 can be found so that the func-

tion $y - c_1 \cos x - c_2 \sin x$ is the identically 0 function.

Thus $y = c_1 \cos x + c_2 \sin x$.

In the proof, we use the theorem of the mean: if a function

has zero derivative on an interval, the function is constant there.

We compute

$$D \{\sin x \cdot Dy - \cos x \cdot y\} = \sin x (D^2 y + y)$$

$$D \{\cos x \cdot Dy + \sin x \cdot y\} = \cos x (D^2 y + y) .$$

By the theorem of the mean, $\sin x \cdot Dy - \cos x \cdot y = -c_1$

$$\cos x \cdot Dy + \sin x \cdot y = c_2$$

The theorem follows if we multiply the first of these equations by

$- \cos x$, the second by $\sin x$, and add.

Corollary 1. Every solution of $[D^2 + \beta^2] y = 0$ has the form

$y = c_1 \cos \beta x + c_2 \sin \beta x$.

A change of independent variables $t = \beta x$ accomplishes the

proof. ∎

Corollary 2. Every solution of $[(D - \alpha)^2 + \beta^2] y = 0$

has the form $y = e^{\alpha x} (c_1 \cos \beta x + c_2 \sin \beta x)$.

This follows from corollary 1, together with lemma 3.

Theorem 1 is a necessary antecedent to theorem 3. Before following that line, we interpose

Theorem 2. Every solution of the d.e. $[(D - a)^p] y = 0$

has the form $y = e^{ax} (c_1 + c_2 x + \ldots + c_p x^{p-1})$.

Proof. By lemma 3, it is enough to consider the case $a = 0$. By the theorem of the mean, every solution of $D y = 0$ has the form $y = \text{const.}$ Suppose it proved that every solution of the d.e. $D^{k-1} y = 0$ has the form

$$y = c_1 + c_2 x + \ldots + c_{k-1} x^{k-2} ;$$

we have to discuss the equation $D^k y = 0$. Writing this equation in the form $D^{k-1} z = 0$, $z = D y$, we see that z must be a polynomial in x of degree $k - 2$ or less. Let y_o be a polynomial of degree $k - 1$ (or less) satisfying $D y_o = z$; there certainly is such a polynomial. Then $D y_o = D y$, so that $D (y - y_o) = 0$, and $y - y_o$ must be a constant; the theorem is proved.

Lemma 6. If r is a nonnegative integer, the d.e.

$$[D^2 + 1] y = x^r \cos x$$

can be satisfied by some linear combination

$$y = y_o = e_1 \ x^r \sin x + f_2 \ x^{r-1} \cos x + \ldots + 1 \cdot (e_{r+1} \cos x + f_{r+1} \sin x).$$

Similarly for the d.e. $[D^2 + 1] y = x^r \sin x$.

For a given numerical value of r, this verification can always be accomplished by determining first e_1, then f_2, then e_3 etc, but this does not constitute a proof. We use induction and suppose that lemma 6 is true for $r = k - 2$. (For $r = 0$, $y_o = \dfrac{1}{2} x \sin x$.)

This means that $[D^2 + 1] y_o = \dfrac{k - 1}{2} x^{k-2} \sin x$ is solvable.

Since

$$[D^2 + 1](x^k \sin x) = -x^k \sin x + 2 k \ x^{k-1} \cos x + k \ (k-1) \ x^{k-2} \sin x +$$
$$+ x^k \sin x,$$

$$[D^2 + 1](x^k \cos x) = -x^k \cos x - 2 k \ x^{k-1} \sin x + k \ (k-1) \ x^{k-2} \cos x +$$
$$+ x^k \cos x,$$

it follows that

$$[D^2 + 1] \ (\dfrac{1}{2k} \ x^k \sin x - y_o) = x^{k-1} \cos x .$$

The induction for $[D^2 + 1] y = x^{k-1} \sin x$ is similar. $\|$

Theorem 3. Every solution of the d.e. $[(D^2 + 1)^p]y = 0$ has

the form

$$y = (c_1\ x^{p-1} + c_2\ x^{p-2} + \ldots + c_p)\ \cos x$$

$$+ (d_1\ x^{p-1} + \ldots \qquad\qquad)\ \sin x\ .$$

The inductive proof depends in an obvious way on lemma 6; see the

proof of theorem 2. ‖

The preceding series of theorems and lemmas taken together

gives a complete account of the nature of the solutions of the

linear d.e. $[f(D)]\ y = 0$, where $f(D)$ is a polynomial with constant

coefficients. For, the more intricate factor $\{(D - \alpha)^2 + \beta^2\}^p$

can be handled by use of lemma 3 and the device in lemma 4. Thus

Theorem 4. Every solution of a linear differential equation

with real constant coefficients and 0 right hand side

$$[f(D)]\ y = 0$$

can be written as a sum of terms of the form

$$x^r\ e^{\alpha x}\ \cos \beta x,\ x^r\ e^{\alpha x}\ \sin \beta x\ ,$$

where α, β are real, $\beta > 0$ and r is a nonnegative integer.

Actually we have proved somewhat more; for example every

solution of $y'' + A y + B = 0$ (where A, B are real) must have

one of the forms

$$e^{ax}\ (c_1 + c_2\ x),\quad c_1\ e^{ax} + c_2\ e^{bx},\quad e^{\alpha x}\ (c_1\ \cos \beta x + c_2\ \sin \beta x)\ .$$

We have not yet shown that the basic solutions of one d.e. do not satisfy another d.e. For example, $x^2 \sin 3x$ does not satisfy

$$\{ (D - \alpha)^2 + \beta^2 \}^p \; y = 0$$

unless p is at least 3, α is 0, and β^2 is 3^2. A sketch of the (general) proof is as follows. First, every collection of basic solutions is linearly independent. For example, if for some constants, c_1, c_2, c_3 the relation

$$c_1 \; x \; e^{2x} + c_2 \cos 3x + c_3 \sin 3x = 0$$

should be valid for all values of x, then there would necessarily be a simpler relation (with fewer terms) also valid, or else the constants are all zero to start with. This can be seen by dropping the zero terms in the first place, and operating on the resulting equation with one of the operators

$$\{ (D - \alpha)^2 + \beta^2 \}^p \quad .$$

(This procedure has to be modified in the sole case that the putative relation reads $c_1 \cos \beta x + c_2 \sin \beta x = 0$.)

Second, if every collection of basic solutions is linearly independent, then $x^2 \sin 3x$ cannot be expressed in the way theorem 3 and the remarks after theorem 3 say it can, unless $\alpha = 0$, $\beta = 3$, $p \geq 3$. ‖

Appendix B

LAPLACE TRANSFORMS

The problem of solving certain classes of differential equations can be replaced by the problem of solving algebraic equations (or problems). Any such process of reduction is called an <u>operator</u> <u>method</u>. Some operator methods use a great deal of shorthand; the Laplace transform method is an example.

Let y be a function of x, with as many derivatives as you wish, all defined for $0 \leq x \leq \infty$. The Laplace transform $L(y)$ of y is the function $\int_0^\infty e^{-sx} y\, dx$, provided this integral is defined. Here are some examples:

Function y	Laplace transform $L(y) = \int_0^\infty e^{-sx} y\, dx$
0	0
1	s^{-1}
x	s^{-2}
$x^k/k!$ $(k > 0$, integer$)$	$s^{-(k+1)}$
e^{ax}	$\dfrac{1}{s-a}$, defined if $s > a$
$x\, e^{ax}$	$\dfrac{1}{(s-a)^2}$

Function y	Laplace transform $L(y) = \int_o^\infty e^{-sx} \, y \, dx$
$x^k e^{ax}/k!$	$\dfrac{1}{(s-a)^{k+1}}$
$\sin x$	$\dfrac{1}{s^2 + 1}$
$\cos x$	$\dfrac{s}{s^2 + 1}$

Also, the Laplace transforms of y' can be found by integration by parts, if y is known to satisfy $\lim_{x \to \infty} y\, e^{-sx} = 0$

for some value of s;

$L(y') = -y(o) + s\, L(y)$. Similarly:

$L(y'') = -y'(o) - s\, y(o) + s^2 L(y)$,

$L(y''') = -y''(o) - s\, y'(o) - s^2 y(o) + s^3 L(y)$.

Example 1. Find the solution y of

(i) $\qquad\qquad y'' - 3y' - 4y = 0$

that satisfies $y(0) = 1$, $y'(0) = -1$.

Solution: The Laplace transform of (i) reads

$$\left[s^2 L(y) - s + 1 \right] - 3 \left[-1 + sL(y) \right] - 4L(y) = 0.$$

Thus

$$L(y) = \frac{-4 + s}{s^2 - 3s - 4} = \frac{A}{s - 4} + \frac{B}{s + 1}$$

To verify the separation into partial fractions, determine

A, B so that

$$A(s + 1) + B(s - 4) = 4 + s, \quad \text{i.e.}$$

$$A + B = 1$$

$$A - 4B = -4 \qquad\qquad A = 0, \quad B = 1$$

Finally,

$$L(y) = \frac{1}{s + 1} ; \quad y = e^{-x}.$$

Example 2. Find the solution y of

(ii) $\qquad\qquad y'' - 3y' - 4y = 12$

that satisfies $y(0) = 1$, $y'(0) = -1$.

Solution: Taking the Laplace transform as in (i), we obtain

$$L(y) = \frac{12}{s(s^2-3s-4)} + \frac{1}{s+1} = \frac{A}{s} + \frac{B}{s-4} + \frac{C}{s+1} + \frac{1}{s+1}$$

$$A(s-4)(s+1) + Bs(s+1) + Cs(s-4) = 12,$$

giving $\qquad\qquad A = -3, \ B = \frac{3}{5}, \ C = \frac{12}{5}$

Thus

$$y = -3 + \frac{3}{5} e^{4x} + \frac{17}{5} e^{-x}.$$

Example 3. Find the solution of

(iii) $\qquad\qquad y'' - 3y' - 4y = 16e^{4x}$

that satisfies $y(0) = 0$, $y'(0) = 1$; also the one for which

$y(0) = 1$, $y'(0) = 0$.

Solution: Taking the Laplace transform with $y(0) = 0$,

$y'(0) = 1$, we obtain

$$[-1 + s^2 \, L(y)] - 3\,[sL(y)] - 4L(y) = 16/(s-4)$$

Thus

$$L(y) = \frac{16}{(s^2-3s-4)(s-4)} + \frac{1}{s^2-3s-4} = \frac{A}{(s-4)^2} + \frac{B}{s-4} + \frac{C}{s+1}.$$

Another device for determining A, B, C is the following.

Multiply both members by $(s-4)^2$, and then let $s \to 4$:

$$\frac{16}{5} = A.$$

Also, multiply both members by $s + 1$, and then let $s \to -1$:

$$\frac{16}{25} + \frac{1}{-5} = C. \quad \text{Thus} \quad C = \frac{11}{25}.$$

Next, let $s = 0$:

$$1 - \frac{1}{4} = \frac{A}{16} + \frac{B}{-4} + C; \quad B = -\frac{11}{25}$$

Thus

$$L(y) = \frac{16/5}{(s-4)^2} + \frac{-11/25}{s-4} + \frac{11/25}{s+1};$$

$$y = \frac{16}{5}\,xe^{4x} - \frac{11}{25}\,e^{4x} + \frac{11}{25}\,e^{-x}.$$

For $y(0) = 1$, $y'(0) = 0$, we find in the same way

$$y = \frac{16}{5}\,xe^{4x} - \frac{11}{25}\,e^{4x} + \frac{36}{25}\,e^{-x}.$$

MISCELLANEOUS FORMULAS

$$\sin (A \pm B) = \sin A \cos B \pm \cos A \sin B$$

$$\cos (A \pm B) = \cos A \cos B \mp \sin A \sin B$$

$$\tan (A \pm B) = \frac{\tan A \pm \tan B}{1 \mp \tan A \tan B}$$

$$\sin 3A = 3 \sin A - 4 \sin^3 A$$

$$\cos 3A = 4 \cos^3 A - 3 \cos A$$

Set $\epsilon_o = \dfrac{1}{2}$, $\epsilon_t = 1 (t > o)$. If p is even,

$$\sin^p A = 2^{-p+1} \sum_{t=o}^{p/2} \epsilon_t (-1)^t \begin{pmatrix} p \\ p/2-t \end{pmatrix} \cos 2tA$$

$\cos^p A =$ same, with factor $(-1)^t$ suppressed.

If p is odd,

$$\sin^p A = 2^{-p+1} \sum_{t=o}^{(p-1)/2} (-1)^t \begin{pmatrix} p \\ (p-1)/2-t \end{pmatrix} \sin(2t+1)A,$$

$$\cos^p A = 2^{-p+1} \sum_{t=o}^{(p-1)/2} \begin{pmatrix} p \\ (p-1)/2-t \end{pmatrix} \cos(2t+1)A .$$

$$\sin A + \sin B = 2 \sin \frac{1}{2} (A + B) \cos \frac{1}{2} (A - B)$$

$$\sin D \cos E = \frac{1}{2} \sin (D + E) + \frac{1}{2} \sin (D - E)$$

$$\sin D \sin E = \frac{1}{2} \cos (D - E) - \frac{1}{2} \cos (D + E)$$

$$\sinh (A + B) = \sinh A \cosh B + \cosh A \sinh B$$

$$\cosh (A + B) = \cosh A \cosh B + \sinh A \sinh B$$

If $A = \cosh B$, than $B = LN (A + \sqrt{A^2 - 1})$

If $A = \sinh B$, than $B = LN (A + \sqrt{A^2 + 1})$

FORMULAS OF DIFFERENTIATION

Function	Derivative (evaluated when independent variable has the value x)
f(x)	$\lim\limits_{h \to 0,\ h \neq 0} \dfrac{f(x + h) - f(x)}{h}$, if this limit exists
Constant	0
x^p	$p\ x^{p-1}$
$\sqrt{x}$	$\dfrac{1}{2\sqrt{x}}$
sin x	cos x
cos x	- sin x
tan x = tg x	(sec x)(sec x)
cotan x = ctg x	- (csc x)(csc x)
sec x	(sec x)(tan x)
cosec x	- (cosec x)(cotan x)
exp x = e^x	exp x
LOG x = LN x	$1/x = x^{-1}$
$\text{LOG}_a x$	$\dfrac{1}{x\ \text{LOG}\ a} = \dfrac{1}{x\ \text{LN}\ a}$
sinh x	cosh x

FORMULAS OF DIFFERENTIATION (Continued)

Function	Derivative (evaluated when independent variable has the value x)
$\cosh x$	$\sinh x$
$\tanh x$	$(\operatorname{sech} x)(\operatorname{sech} x)$
$\operatorname{Arcsin} x$	$\dfrac{1}{\sqrt{1 - x^2}}$
$\operatorname{Arccos} x$	$\dfrac{-1}{\sqrt{1 - x^2}}$
$\operatorname{Arctan} x$	$\dfrac{1}{1 + x^2}$
$\operatorname{Arctanh} x$	$\dfrac{1}{1 - x^2}$
$\operatorname{Arcsinh} x$	$\dfrac{1}{\sqrt{1 + x^2}}$
$\operatorname{Arccosh} x$	$\dfrac{1}{\sqrt{x^2 - 1}}$
$u\,v$	$u\,v' + u'\,v$
$u/v = u\,v^{-1}$	$(u'v - u\,v')\,v^{-2}$
$u^m\,v^n$	$(n\,u\,v' + m\,u'\,v)(u^{m-1}\,v^{n-1})$

$$D_x u = (D_t u)(D_x t)$$

SOME COMMON INTEGRALS

Function of u	Integral of the function with respect to u: $\int f(u)\,du$
0	C = arbitrary constant
u^p (p≠-1)	$u^{p+1}/(p+1)$ + C
u^{-1}	LN $\lvert u \rvert$ + C
sin u	- cos u + C
cos u	sin u + C
tan u = tg u	LN $\lvert$ sec u $\rvert$ + C
cotan u = ctg u	LN $\lvert$ sin u $\rvert$ + C
sec u	LN $\lvert$ sec u + tan u $\rvert$ + C
csc u	LN $\lvert$ csc u - ctn u $\rvert$ + C
exp u = e^u	exp u + C
LN u	u LN u - u + C
sinh u	cosh u + C
cosh u	sinh u + C
tanh u = sinh u/cosh u	LN cosh u + C
cotanh u = cosh u/sinh u	LN $\lvert$ sinh u $\rvert$ + C
$\cos^2 u$	$\frac{1}{2} u + \frac{1}{4}$ sin 2 u + C

SOME COMMON INTEGRALS (Continued)

Function of u	Integral of the function with respect to u: $\int f(u)\,du$
$\sin^2 u = 1 - \cos^2 u$	$\dfrac{1}{2} u - \dfrac{1}{4} \sin 2u + C$
$\sin u \cos u = \dfrac{1}{2} \sin 2u$	$-\dfrac{1}{4} \cos 2u \qquad + C$
$\dfrac{1}{a + bu}$	$LN\left\lvert\, a + bu \,\right\rvert^{1/b} + C$
$\dfrac{1}{a^2 - b^2 u^2}$	$\dfrac{1}{2ab}\ LN\left\lvert \dfrac{a + bu}{a - bu} \right\rvert$
	$= \dfrac{1}{ab}\ \text{Arc tanh}\ \dfrac{bu}{a} + C$
$\dfrac{1}{\sqrt{a^2 - b^2 u^2}}\quad (a > o)$	$\dfrac{1}{b}\ \text{Arc sin}\ \dfrac{bu}{a} + C$
$\dfrac{1}{a^2 + b^2 u^2}$	$\dfrac{1}{ab}\ \text{Arc tan}\ \dfrac{bu}{a} + C$
$\dfrac{1}{\sqrt{a^2 + b^2 u^2}}\quad (a > o)\,.$	$\dfrac{1}{b}\ \text{Arc sinh}\ \dfrac{bu}{a} + C$
	$= \dfrac{1}{b}\ LN\left\lvert \sqrt{a^2 + b^2 u^2} + bu \right\rvert + C$
	$= -\dfrac{1}{b}\ LN\left\lvert \sqrt{a^2 + b^2 u^2} - bu \right\rvert + C_1$
$\dfrac{1}{\sqrt{b^2 u^2 - a^2}}\quad (a > o)$	$\dfrac{1}{b}\ \text{Arc cosh}\ \dfrac{bu}{a} + C$
	$= \dfrac{1}{b}\ LN\left\lvert \sqrt{b^2 u^2 - a^2} + bu \right\rvert + C$

SQUARE ROOTS - CUBE ROOTS

N	$\sqrt{N}$	$\sqrt{10N}$	$\sqrt[3]{N}$	$\sqrt[3]{10N}$	$\sqrt[3]{100N}$
0.1	0.316	1.	.464	1.	2.154
0.15	.387	1.225	.531	1.145	2.467
0.2	.447	1.414	.585	1.260	2.714
0.25	.5	1.581	.630	1.357	2.924
0.3	.548	1.732	.669	1.442	3.107
0.4	.632	2.	.739	1.587	3.420
0.5	.707	2.236	.794	1.710	3.684
0.6	.775	2.449	.843	1.817	3.915
0.7	.837	2.646	.888	1.913	4.121
0.8	.894	2.828	.928	2.	4.309
0.9	0.949	3.	.965	2.080	4.481
1.0	1.	3.162	1.	2.154	4.641

$\pi = 3.14159$ $e = 2.71828$

$\pi^2 = 9.870$

LOGARITHMS

N	$\text{LOG}_e N = \text{LN } N$	$\text{LOG}_{10} N$
0.01	$-$ 4.605	
0.05	$-$ 2.996	
0.1	$-$ 2.303	
0.5	$-$ 0.693	
1	$+$ 0	0
1.5	+0.40547	.1761
2	+0.69315	.3010
2.5	+0.91629	.3979
e	+1.	0.43429
3	+1.09861	.4771
π	+1.14473	.4971
4	+1.38629	.6021
5	+1.60944	.6990
6	+1.79176	.7781
7	+1.94951	.8451
8	+2.08944	.9031
9	+2.19722	.9542
10	+2.30259	1.
100	+4.60517	
1000	+6.9077	

$$\text{LOG}_e N = (2.30259) \text{LOG}_{10} N$$

EXPONENTIALS

$$\text{EXP } N = 1 + N + \frac{N^2}{2} + \frac{N^3}{6} + \ldots$$

$$\text{EXP } -N = 1 - N + \frac{N^2}{2} - \frac{N^3}{6} + \ldots$$

0.01	1.0101	.9901
2	1.0202	.9802
3	1.0305	.9704
4	1.0408	.9608
5	1.0513	.9512
6	1.0618	.9418
7	1.0725	.9324
8	1.0833	.9231
0.09	1.0942	.9139
0.1	1.1052	.9048
2	1.2214	.8187
3	1.3499	.7408
4	1.4918	.6703
5	1.6487	.6065
6	1.8221	.5488
7	2.0138	.4966
8	2.2255	.4493
0.9	2.4596	.4066
1.	2.7183	.3679
2.	7.3891	.1353
3.	20.086	.0498
4.	54.598	.0183
5.	148.41	.0067
6.	403.43	.0025
7.	1096.6	.0009
8.	2981.0	.0003
9.	8103.	.00012
10.	22026.	.00004

TRIGONOMETRIC FUNCTIONS

RADIAN VALUES OF THE ARGUMENT

t	SIN t	COS t	TAN t	CTN t	SEC t	CSC t
0.1	+.0998	+.9950	+ .1003	9.97	1.005	10.02
.2	.1987	.9801	.2027	4.93	1.020	5.033
.3	.2955	.9553	.3093	3.23	1.047	3.384
.4	.3894	.9211	.4228	2.37	1.086	2.568
.5	.4794	.8776	.5463	1.83	1.139	2.086
.6	.5646	.8253	.6841	1.462	1.212	1.771
.7	.6442	.7648	.8423	1.187	1.307	1.552
.8	.7174	.6967	1.030	.9712	1.435	1.394
0.9	.7833	.6216	1.260	.7936	1.609	1.277
1.0	.8415	.5403	1.557	.6421	1.851	1.188
1.1	.8912	.4536	1.965	.5090	2.205	1.122
1.2	.9320	.3624	2.57	.3888	2.760	1.073
1.3	.9636	.2675	3.60	.2776	3.738	1.038
1.4	.9854	.1700	5.80	.1725	5.883	1.015
1.5	.9975	+.0707	14.1	.0709	14.14	1.003
1.6	+.9996	-.0292	-34.	-.0292	-34.25	1.000
1.7	.9917	-.1288	- 7.70	-.1299	- 7.761	1.008
1.8	.9738	-.2272	- 4.29	-.2333	- 4.401	1.027
1.9	.9463	-.3233	- 2.93	-.3416	- 3.093	1.057
2.0	.9093	-.4161	- 2.19	-.4577	- 2.403	1.100
2.1	.8632	-.5048	- 1.710	-.5848	- 1.981	1.158
2.2	.8085	-.5885	- 1.374	-.7279	- 1.699	1.237
2.5	+.5985	-.8011	- .7470	-1.339	- 1.248	1.671
3.0	+.1411	-.9900	- .1425	-7.02	- 1.010	7.086
3.5	-.3508	-.9365	.3746	2.67	- 1.068	-2.851
4.0	-.7568	-.6536	1.158	.8637	- 1.530	-1.321
4.5	-.9775	-.2108	4.64	.2156	- 4.744	-1.023
5.0	-.9589	+.2837	-3.38	- .2958	3.525	-1.043

1 RAD = 180/π DEG = 57. 29578 DEG = 206 264.81 SECONDS OF ARC

3J1104